PEN

B

'A true climate leade . . . Sadiq recognises that
the struggles for social justice and climate justice cannot
be separated but go hand-in-hand.'
Ed Miliband

'Since his election, Mayor Sadiq Khan has shown the world
that transformative green politics is possible.'
Justin Trudeau, Prime Minister of Canada

'If you want to build a greener world, you need to
win people round to green politics. This remarkable
book offers a transformative insight into how.'
Anne Hidalgo, Mayor of Paris

'Cities are where we will lose or win the climate
change battle. This book offers a compelling torch of
light on the path forward.'
Christiana Figueres, former Executive Secretary,
United Nations Framework Convention on Climate Change

'Hilarious, uplifting and yet often unexpectedly moving, *Breathe*
reveals what life as Mayor is really like – and offers powerful tools
for anyone who wants to win the argument on climate.'
Edward Enninful

'Combines laugh-out-load anecdotes with real insight into
delivering effective action for climate . . . An absolute must read
for anyone interested in politics for progressive change.'
Jemima Hartshorn, co-founder, Mums for Lungs

'A warm, optimistic, urgent call for change.'
Sathnam Sanghera, author of *Empireland*

'This funny, thoughtful and empowering book is filled
with fascinating glimpses into life at City Hall . . . A powerful
and practical riposte to anyone losing hope in the ability of
politicians to tackle the climate crisis.'
Ed Balls

'It doesn't get much more fundamental than our right to
breathe clean air and Sadiq Khan's hard-hitting book propels
this issue into our consciousness.'
Thomas Heatherwick

'An accessible, salutary read – well-written and
sprinkled with anecdotes.'
The House

'Very hopeful and interesting.'
Richard Herring

'Inspiring, passionate, a great read!'
Sarah Woolnough, former CEO, Asthma + Lung UK

'Quite the page-turner.'
Evening Standard

'By working together and sharing our experiences we can make a
real difference globally, and in this book Sadiq sets out our shared
commitment to tackling the urgent challenge of the climate
crisis, congestion and toxic air pollution.'
Beppe Sala, Mayor of Milan

'Positions cities as indispensable actors in the fight for a green and inclusive future.'
Valerie Plante, Mayor of Montreal

'Warm, thoughtful and humorous.'
Riz Ahmed

'This educational yet entertaining book sets out how it is possible for all cities to not just tackle the climate crisis but thrive at the same time.'
Mark Watts, Executive Director, C40 Cities

'Well-written, sometimes amusing . . . Half memoir, half manifesto, it positions him as Britain's ultra-green politician.'
The Times

'A revelation. This book offers uplifting solutions to climate fatalism – bringing Sadiq's trademark wit and warmth to point the way to a greener world.'
David Miller, former Mayor of Toronto

'Sadiq's outstanding leadership on climate change has put London at the forefront of the global effort to stop it. This book shows the importance of doing more, faster.'
Mike Bloomberg, former Mayor of New York City

'A roadmap to a greener world for all of us.'
Kate Gallego, Mayor of Phoenix

'Seeks to empower people throughout Britain and beyond to take proactive action against pollution and climate change.'
Reader's Digest

'One of our leading green politicians reveals how to defuse the argument of any climate naysayer, starting now.'
Yvonne Aki-Sawyerr, Mayor of Freetown

'Incredibly accessible and personal narrative. A joy and a fun read, deeds and words on the most important and ongoing danger of our time.'
Helen Pankhurst CBE

'Politically courageous . . . an example for all mayors around the world.'
Dr Maria Neira, Director, Public Health and Environment, WHO

'A story in which the personal meets the political.'
Perspective

'An eye-opening insight into what it's like trying to fight for the planet from inside the decision-makers.'
IFL Science

'This shows the world that mayors can and should use health as an argument to improve living environments.'
Dr Tedros Adhanom Ghebreyesus, Director-General, WHO

'A passionate read that evidently has Londoners' interests at heart. *Breathe* will surely inspire other city leaders across the world to follow suit.'
Professor Frank J. Kelly FRSB FRSC FMedSci, Head of the Environmental Research Group, Imperial College

'Viscerally potent, yet lucidly argued.'
North East Post

Breathe

How to Win
a Greener
World

Sadiq Khan

PENGUIN BOOKS

For Anisah and Ammarah

PENGUIN BOOKS

UK | USA | Canada | Ireland | Australia
India | New Zealand | South Africa

Penguin Books is part of the Penguin Random House group of companies
whose addresses can be found at global.penguinrandomhouse.com

First published by Hutchinson Heinemann 2023
Published in Penguin Books 2024

001

Copyright © Sadiq Khan, 2023
Afterword copyright © Sadiq Khan, 2024

The moral right of the author has been asserted

Typeset in 12.96/15.4pt Garamond MT Std by Jouve (UK), Milton Keynes
Printed and bound in Great Britain by Clays Ltd, Elcograf S.p.A.

The authorised representative in the EEA is Penguin Random House Ireland,
Morrison Chambers, 32 Nassau Street, Dublin D02 YH68

A CIP catalogue record for this book is available from the British Library

ISBN: 978-1-804-94011-2

www.greenpenguin.co.uk

MIX
Paper | Supporting
responsible forestry
FSC® C018179

Penguin Random House is committed to a
sustainable future for our business, our readers
and our planet. This book is made from Forest
Stewardship Council® certified paper.

Contents

Introduction

Ella's Story

I ran for London before I actually ran for London.

It was the summer of 2011, and I had invited a journalist from the *Evening Standard*, David Cohen, to visit my constituency office in Tooting Bec, South London. A few weeks previously, the police's shooting of Mark Duggan had triggered riots in Tottenham, which soon spread to other parts of London and then the country. David was writing a series of articles about the riots and was keen to get my perspective as a London MP.

As part of the interview, we had decided to travel up to Battersea, where some of the rioting had taken place. We found ourselves sprinting a fair distance for the bus. As we sat on the top deck panting, David and I complimented one another for making it as two middle-aged dads. I discovered that David was actually a regular marathon runner. It was one of the ways he helped the *Standard* raise money for its 'Dispossessed Fund', which supported vulnerable people from across the capital.

We kept in touch and in early 2014, David contacted me to tell me the paper had been trying to persuade the then-Labour MP and Shadow Chancellor Ed Balls to run the London Marathon for the Dispossessed Fund. But Ed had already agreed to run for Action for Stammering Children and Whizz-Kidz. He had suggested my name as an alternative because I'd taken on a new job as shadow minister for London. As David reminisced about our run for the bus back in Tooting, I realised where the conversation was going.

'Have you got an alibi?' The question I'd asked dozens of times in my former life as a lawyer was now turned on me.

I tried a few excuses: 'I am not a runner.' 'I don't have the right kit.' 'Twenty-six-point-two miles is a really long way!' But David was unconvinced. Before I knew it, my wife, Saadiya – who was still a criminal defence lawyer and so took great pleasure in asking me the alibi question – was weighing in, trying to persuade me to run. She played to my competitive streak: if Ed Balls could run a marathon, surely I could?

Things escalated when my political advisor Jack Stenner and head of office Ali Picton got wind of the idea. They were also keen. Partly, I suspected, so they could have a few hours off from my text messages while I was training. But also because they were pushing for me to run in an even longer race – to become the Labour candidate for the upcoming London mayoral election. They knew that the editor of the *Standard*, Sarah Sands, was very close to the MP who was favourite to become the Labour candidate, my colleague and friend Tessa Jowell.

Any opportunity to go the extra mile (the pun was excruciating even then) to build my relationship with the paper was invaluable. It didn't help that Ali had run the London Marathon several times and was evangelical about it. She took a leaf out of David's rhetorical playbook. If she could run a marathon, surely I could?

Eventually, I relented. After all, I thought, I was reasonably fit. I played football with a group of friends every Sunday. I only overindulged my weakness for a Snickers bar occasionally. How hard could it be? I tried not to take offence at the speed everyone's enthusiasm about me running the Marathon turned to concern about my health once I told them I might actually do it. My friend, local GP and marathon-runner extraordinaire Tom Coffey, was given strict instructions to provide me with a full medical, and keep a close eye on my training to ensure I didn't inadvertently die.

On a cold Sunday in February, 70 days before race day, I laced up my trainers and headed out on my first run in advance of the Marathon. Having started training late, I was on a strict regime. So it was worrying to discover that I wasn't quite as fit as I had imagined. After only a mile or two, I felt terrible and was convinced I was going to have to stop to throw up – not the best look for the local MP. After about half an hour, though, I started to get into the swing of things. Several laps of Tooting Common later I felt pretty smug about having run a decent seven miles. Much further than I had expected.

The smugness didn't last long. I can't describe the pain I was in the next day. Hobbling around Parliament, I tried to hide my stiffness and my limp from other MPs whom I hadn't yet told about my new project. My parliamentary office was usually a good five minutes' walk from the House of Commons Chamber, where I was required to vote several times a day. I was on high alert for the sound of the division bells which ring across Parliament for eight minutes before the doors to the voting lobbies are closed. I wasn't always sure I'd make it in time.

Ed Balls wasn't my only competition in the Palace of Westminster. In 2014 a record number of MPs were planning to run the London Marathon – eight of us – and half of those were around the Shadow Cabinet table: Ed, Shadow Health Secretary Andy Burnham, Shadow International Development Secretary Jim Murphy (who later dropped out due to injury) and me. It was Ed's third Marathon and I knew from experience that a few weeks before the race, he would become unbearable: you would hear of nothing else. For my part, I was deliberately keeping my decision low-profile in case I decided to pull out. It would have been embarrassing if people had known.

Much to my horror, only a week after I began my training, Ed told the audience at a packed Labour fundraiser dinner that not only was he running the Marathon (again) but that I would be joining him. People clearly thought it was a joke as it was the biggest laugh Ed got in his speech. This did not do much for my confidence.

While I didn't admit it to Ed (he would have been insufferable), I learned a lot from his advice – and within a few weeks, training was going well. I had the right kit, good trainers, and an upbeat playlist featuring master-pieces ranging from 'Eye of the Tiger' to the *Rocky* theme. After my training sessions I'd often text Jack, Ali and my policy advisor Dr Nick Bowes, fizzing with ideas that had come to me while running. So much for the Marathon giving them a break from my messages.

Before I knew it, it was the day of the race. As I stood on the start-line with David and my fellow *Evening Standard* runners in Greenwich Park, my nerves were worse than any election night I'd experienced. Our bags were packed in a truck to be taken to the finish line, and I handed my phone over to Ali, who at this point was the only person more terrified than I was.

And then we were off.

Despite the pain, I got a lot out of running the Marathon. By the time we reached the Thames and wove our way around the *Cutty Sark*, even if I wasn't quite enjoying myself, I was starting to see why you might. Any time you feel you can't carry on, the cheers of the crowd pull you through. I had a brief ego-trip when I noticed that people were shouting my name on every mile of the race – clearly my profile-building had gone better than

I'd thought – before I realised they do that for everyone by reading the name off your T-shirt.

My knees started hurting by around mile 15, but the adrenaline kept me going. I was determined not only to finish, but not to walk any of the way. By mile 23 I had run further than I had ever run before and was really struggling. Among the voices cheering me on, one with a distinct Northern twang calling out, 'Go on, Sadiq!' sounded familiar. I didn't have the energy to look around – but I felt a tap on the shoulder and a figure started running alongside me: my friend Ben Johnson, a Tooting councillor who had come with me to get my kit just days earlier. Ben had run several Marathons before and had been encouraging me in the week building up to the big day, when I had been incredibly anxious. He ran by my side for a mile or so, encouraging me every step of the way. I felt guilty slowing him down, but his support was exactly what I needed. At around mile 24, I spotted some friends on the sidelines, and got a second wind. I told Ben to run on, which after some persuading he did. At last, thanks to Ben's help, the end was in sight.

Crossing the finish line of the London Marathon is a special moment – deeply personal, but also a shared experience with the other 40,000 people who are taking part. There is a great photo of me biting the gold-coloured medal I was given on finishing, just as I had seen my heroes do on television during the Olympics (although I looked a bit more bedraggled after 26.2 miles than they did). As it turned out, 2014 was the year the double Olympic gold medallist Mo Farah ran his first London Marathon too. To this day, I often tell people that I raced Mo Farah. I don't volunteer that I finished two hours behind him.

As I stood panting at the race's end, I couldn't help basking in how far I'd come in the last ten weeks. I had completed the Marathon in 4 hours 19 minutes, well under my five-hour target. I had raised more than £20,000 for the Dispossessed Fund. I had even beaten Ed Balls *and* Andy Burnham.

Over the next few weeks, I found myself reflecting that the Marathon embodies everything that makes London special. The route passes through five very different boroughs: from the high streets of Woolwich and Deptford, through Canary Wharf skyscrapers, and then on to the Houses of Parliament. More than anything, though, the experience taught me that I actually liked running. I was fitter than I had been in a long time, and lighter too. In the weeks and months that followed, I carried on pounding the pavements of London. Not immediately, of course: I was in too much pain. After a few months, though, I was back out there as much as my schedule allowed.

But the Marathon wasn't just the beginning of my journey as a runner. It was also, unexpectedly, the beginning of my journey as a climate activist.

As I got more and more into jogging, I started to

encounter a new problem. After a long run, I would find myself wheezing and struggling to breathe. At first, I put it down to a lack of fitness. But the wheezing turned into coughing, and was soon being noticed by my family, friends and my team, particularly in the months leading up to the 2015 general election. They pointed out that I kept clearing my throat, at times almost constantly – to the extent that it was undermining my performance during live radio interviews.

Any boundaries I might have had about discussing health issues with my staff had gone out the window when I sought their advice on how to solve my 'runner's nipple' problem during Marathon training. So we talked over what to do. At first, life felt too frantic to get it checked out – shortly after the election in May 2015 I'd launched my official campaign to be Labour's London mayoral candidate, and was working round the clock. I assumed my poor health was a result of being run-down and working long hours. But by September, my excuses had worn thin. I gave in and went to see my GP.

Saadiya insisted on coming with me as she was worried I would tell the GP I was fine and wouldn't fully explain the symptoms. I walked in feeling relaxed, with no expectation of anything more than a clean bill of health and of putting Saadiya's mind at ease.

After a few quick tests, I received the diagnosis of 'adult-onset asthma'.

I was incredulous. Growing up, I had had a few friends

who'd used an asthma inhaler and hadn't really played sports with the rest of us as a result. But I was 43 years old. I'd never had any breathing or respiratory issues. I'd just run a marathon, for goodness' sake. My GP took the time to explain that it wasn't uncommon now for people to develop the condition in adulthood, largely due to environmental factors like poor air quality.

There had been no trace of this when I'd had a full medical before the Marathon. I had almost certainly developed it from the air I was breathing while training on London's roads.

As she talked me through the diagnosis, everything started to make sense. I felt a sense of relief: at least now I knew what the problem was. In the days that followed I felt a sense of relief physically too, as the asthma inhalers and medicine started to make a difference. I could finally get a decent night's sleep, and I found using the inhaler before or during a long run or a game of football really helped. But I wasn't happy about my newfound identity as an asthma patient. Perhaps, on one level, I didn't like to recognise that I was 'vulnerable'; my asthma felt like a sign of weakness. To this day, there are times when it gets so bad I struggle to breathe. A mayoral trip to Delhi in 2017 was made almost impossible due to the terrible-quality air.

But the biggest change resulting from my diagnosis was to my political outlook. I found it hard to believe that my asthma was a direct result of breathing in the city I loved. Had I known that my Sunday-afternoon runs along Balham High Road were causing permanent and lasting damage to my health, would I have stuck to the gym instead?

More importantly, the diagnosis made me think about many issues I had never really considered. Had the air we breathed always been this bad? How many people were affected? Was air pollution linked to climate change? And, if so, would cleaning up London's air help tackle the climate crisis too?

Until then, I had never been particularly 'green'. When I was offered a salaried partnership in a law firm, I had negotiated a car parking space for my Saab convertible on the same street as the office in Central London. After my eldest daughter, Anisah, was born, I had upgraded to a more spacious Land Rover Discovery: a huge gas-guzzling vehicle that spent almost its entire life being driven around the capital. As a Member of Parliament, I had even voted for a new third runway at Heath-row Airport. Climate change had always seemed very far away – both geographically and temporally. It was a 'tomorrow' issue rather than a 'today' issue.

Asthma made me think again. After my trip to the doctor, I began to notice the cars idling outside schools and the exhaust fumes streaming out of vehicles in grid-locked traffic – as well as the wildfires on the news that had begun to rage across Europe as a result of increased temperatures. Environmental problems weren't just causing problems 'out there'; they had just given me asthma, here in London. This wasn't just a climate crisis, it was a health crisis.

I also learned that having an asthma attack is scary. And I'm an adult. I can rationalise what's happening to me when my chest gets tight and I find it hard to breathe. I can reach for my asthma inhaler, or ask someone to get it for me.

I can't imagine how frightening it must be for a child. And there is no better way to demonstrate exactly why our toxic air matters than the story of Ella Roberta Adoo-Kissi-Debrah.

Like me, Ella was born in South London. Her potential shone bright from a young age. She attended a performing arts school from the age of three and loved to dance and sing. *Mamma Mia!* was her favourite film. At school she was well liked and enjoyed sports and science. She dreamed of becoming a pilot.

Just before her seventh birthday, during the October half-term holiday, Ella began to develop a cough. Her mum, Rosamund, had taken her to the Monument in Central London, as part of her school project on the Great Fire of London. Ella became breathless climbing the stairs. Determined to make it to the top, she persevered, falling fast asleep with exhaustion on the train ride home. Worried, Rosamund took her to the doctor.

The initial diagnosis from her GP was a chest infection,

and Ella was prescribed antibiotics with the expectation of a full recovery. Recovery never came, and in the weeks that followed she had a range of tests, for everything from cystic fibrosis to epilepsy, before eventually being diagnosed by a series of specialist doctors with a unique and severe form of asthma. Her condition was complex, leading to a continuous build-up of mucus in her lungs that reduced air flow. The lack of oxygen would cause Ella to faint, have seizures, and ultimately resulted in her lungs collapsing completely. A few months later, she was admitted into intensive care, for what was to be the first of several visits.

In the 28-month period following her diagnosis, Ella was admitted to hospital 27 times. Her mum resuscitated her on over 20 occasions, and she was treated in five separate hospitals and by numerous specialists.

On Valentine's Day evening in 2013, Ella sat with her mum reading Beethoven's famous love letters. The next day was the last day before half-term, and together they picked out Ella's outfit for the school disco. It was to be their last night together. A few hours later, she stopped breathing. Ella had a seizure in the ambulance, and died in hospital in the early hours of 15 February. She was nine years old.

Ella's story is every parent's worst nightmare. I can't comprehend how scared she and her family must have been throughout. But for Rosamund, her death also raised a number of questions. What had really happened to her daughter? Why had she developed asthma, and what had made it so difficult for her to breathe? Could her condition have been prevented? The pathologist who carried out her post-mortem said Ella had suffered from 'one of the worst cases of asthma ever recorded in the UK', and the coroner who investigated her death concluded she had died due to a severe asthma attack followed by a seizure, 'possibly caused by a reaction to something in the air'.[1] But what?

It was not until many months later that a neighbour mentioned to Rosamund that their neighbourhood in Lewisham often had particularly poor air quality, due to its location near the busy South Circular Road. This was the first time that Rosamund had considered that pollution might have contributed to Ella's death. Medical staff had never suggested this during her multiple hospital visits and admissions. She hadn't imagined that Ella's condition could be linked to the air she was breathing every day. Why would it?

So began the journey to find out the truth about what had really happened to Ella. In January 2014, less than a year after her death – and around the same time I started training for the London Marathon – the Ella Roberta Foundation was created.

Over the next few months, the foundation worked to improve the lives of children affected by asthma in South-East London by raising awareness, calling for better treatment for lung conditions, and campaigning for clean air. As the organisation's co-founder and executive director, Rosamund quickly became a trusted advocate for parents of children with asthma during discussions with clinicians and policymakers. But without the relevant scientific knowledge – and amid a dearth of accurate information about London's air – Rosamund couldn't hope to uncover the truth about Ella's death.

It wasn't until I was elected Mayor of London in May 2016 that I learned of Ella's case. But the moment I heard the story, I knew it was important. It was just like one of the cases I would have taken on in my past life as a lawyer. Before becoming an MP, I had specialised in human rights law. That often meant challenging public authorities like the national government, local authorities, the police and the NHS. I had often represented people with backgrounds similar to mine. When I brought a discrimination case or called for judicial review on a government decision, I remembered that, in a parallel world, the client could have been my family, my neighbours – or me.

So Ella's story struck a nerve. But for the grace of God, my mum could have been Rosamund. Thankfully, my asthma was nowhere near as bad as Ella's. But how many children like Ella were there? And it seemed Ella had been let down by the authorities, just like my old clients had. She had died in the same year the mayoral authority in City Hall had chosen not to publish a report they had commissioned from environmental consultants

Aether, which had set out the dire state of pollution in the capital. Rosamund had had no idea that the air her daughter was breathing was making her sick, and she hadn't been given the chance to find out.

I asked my team to contact Rosamund to see how we could support her. We soon discovered that we had friends and supporters in common. Samantha Heath, a London Assembly Member whom I knew from our time together on Wandsworth Council, introduced us to one another at an event in City Hall. Sam also introduced me to Professor Stephen Holgate, one of the UK's foremost experts on air pollution and asthma. By this time, Rosamund had persuaded a campaigning lawyer called Jocelyn Cockburn to take on the case. I also knew Jocelyn well – she had worked for me at my old law firm.

The four of us – Rosamund, Stephen, Jocelyn and I – began to cooperate. After Ella's death, given the questions she had about what had happened, Rosamund had asked staff at Great Ormond Street Hospital to take tissue samples of her daughter's body. She now gave Stephen access to these samples, and to all of Ella's medical records. In the months that followed, Stephen examined all the data. He was able to rule out most of the typical causes of asthma in children – including allergies and exposure to viruses. And he established that Ella had a form of asthma that made her particularly sensitive to the air she breathed. When looking under the microscope at some of the tissues from Ella's airways and lungs at the time of her death, he discovered that her airways were severely damaged.

Professor Holgate's findings started to shed light on what had gone wrong in Ella's final year. He found a clear correlation between spikes in air pollution near the family home and Ella's admissions to hospital. Readings from pollution monitors close to where the family lived showed that levels of nitrogen dioxide regularly exceeded legal limits, as well as World Health Organization (WHO) and European Union guidelines, primarily because of emissions from diesel vehicles on the South Circular. On the night Ella had died their community had been covered by an invisible fog of fumes from the nearby traffic.

Stephen's 2018 report identified the 'striking association' between Ella's hospital admissions and the most dangerous episodes of air pollution around her home in South-East London.[2] He concluded that there was a clear connection between Ella's health and levels of toxic pollutants, such as nitrogen dioxide and particulate matter, and that Ella's death certificate should reflect air pollution as a causative factor. He said there was a 'real prospect that without unlawful levels of air pollution, Ella would not have died'.[3]

So began Rosamund's campaign to quash the existing coroner's ruling, and have a new inquest into Ella's death. 'Air pollution' had never appeared on a British death certificate. Ella's case would be a legal first – certainly in the UK, and maybe on the planet. If air pollution were to be cited as a cause of death, the coroner could also potentially demand that the national government, and other tiers of local government like mayors and councils, take steps to prevent future deaths. The potential impact of the decision was enormous. Thankfully, following requests from me, Rosamund's lawyers and various campaign groups, the UK's attorney general agreed to review the evidence, and backed the application for a new inquest.

They say a week is a long time in politics. Unfortunately you can't say the same of the legal world. Eight years after Ella's death, and four years after my election as Mayor, we finally got a verdict. But when it came, it was transformative. In December 2020, Coroner Philip Barlow concluded that toxic air had indeed played a role in Ella's death. She became the first person in the UK to ever have 'air pollution' listed as a cause of death.

The coroner's findings had finally answered Ella's family's questions. But the effects of his report were felt far more widely. As the first legal recognition that air pollution had contributed to the death of an individual, the ruling paved the way for others who wanted to see further action on air quality. It gave us concrete evidence that toxicity from transport doesn't just stunt children's lungs – it is a killer.

Above all, the inquest verdict hammered home why it was important to take the environment seriously. Ella's case showed that the lives of Londoners were being harmed by the very act that keeps us alive: breathing.

Life is powered by breath. Our lungs fuel us with oxygen, and pass it through our blood, from where it's transported to the organs that allow us to walk, talk and move. To live.

But while we all breathe, we don't all breathe the same air. Air is made up of about 78 per cent nitrogen, 21 per cent oxygen, and small amounts of other gases like carbon dioxide, helium and hydrogen. It's also made up of a number of pollutants. Where the air is polluted, it can damage every organ and cell in our bodies. It contributes to illnesses ranging from heart and lung disease to diabetes and dementia, from cancer to brittle bones, from damaged skin to asthma. The World Health Organization has called air pollution a public health emergency, with 99 per cent of the global population breathing toxic air.[4] The nine million early deaths it causes each year makes air pollution a bigger killer than tobacco smoking.[5] These deaths are disproportionately concentrated among the most disadvantaged people in society. More than 90 per cent of air pollution-related deaths occur in low- and middle-income countries, where laws are ineffective or not upheld, vehicle emission standards are less strict, and fossil-fuel-burning is more widespread.[6]

The main causes of poor air quality are also the causes of climate breakdown. Air pollution and global warming are largely caused by the same thing: greenhouse gases, particularly from transport, industry and power generation. Energy production – the main cause of greenhouse gas emissions – causes 85 per cent of airborne particulate pollution and almost 100 per cent of nitrogen oxide emissions.[7] This means the solutions to air pollution and climate change are often the same. Tackle one, and you tackle both.

And yet, until my Marathon experience – and my first meetings with Rosamund – I'd barely known about air pollution. I wasn't alone. Why don't we talk about this more? I wondered.

One reason might be that climate change and air pollution are largely invisible killers. Citizens can't see them. And that means politicians can ignore them. Although governments across the world are fond of setting targets, the policies to hit them often fail to materialise. In some cases, government policies actively increase emissions. The UK continues to subsidise fossil fuels. Norway is developing huge new oil and gas fields. Japan remains one of the biggest funders of overseas coal. China continues to build large coal-fired power stations week on week. Tough action on climate, many politicians think, is the triple whammy: an unsolvable problem, which doesn't really matter in the here and now, and which will lose you votes.

This book is my attempt to convince politicians and voters otherwise.

I'd be the first to admit that I've made mistakes as mayor. A few of them are described in this book in agonising detail (for me, at least). But the area where I feel proudest of my record – and most adamant we've got things right – is on the environment.

London was one of the first cities in the world to declare a climate emergency. We've introduced the world's first Ultra Low Emission Zone (ULEZ) – an area where a fee is charged for driving the most polluting vehicles – which has reduced toxic air pollution in Central London by nearly half. Since my election in 2016, London has seen a 94 per cent reduction in the number of people living in areas with illegal levels of nitrogen dioxide. As a result, London is expected to meet legal pollution limits by 2025, as opposed to the 193-year wait predicted when I entered office. And that's not to mention the 440,000 trees we've planted, the fivefold increase in the number of cycle lanes we've overseen, the record number of electric charging points and the biggest fleet of zero-emission buses in Europe.

We didn't just foist these changes on the people of London. London voted for them. During my re-election campaign in 2021, I stood on a platform that put green issues front and centre: including a pledge to expand the ULEZ to cover the massive area within the North and South Circular roads. We won with record numbers of votes for any sitting mayor. Four million Londoners living within the expanded zone are now breathing cleaner air.

So in this book, I want to tell you a story. It's a story about how I went from being a Land Rover driver to an electric bike evangelist. It's a story about working with experts, Londoners and mayors across the globe to tackle an issue that matters to all of us. But above all, it's a story about how I realised that climate change isn't political kryptonite. The case for tough action on the environment is one that concerned citizens, activists and politicians can win. And once it's won, we can start to make things better.

I'm under no illusions: this is the story of one mayor, in one city, standing on one platform. But over the last few years, I've spoken to countless people – from voters and activists to politicians and my fellow mayors around the world – who've talked about running into the same problems I encountered when trying to win the argument on climate change.

They talk about the problem of apathy: the hard slog of getting voters to care about the environment in the face of the more pressing concerns that define their lives. They talk about cynicism: the ever-present sense that politicians are 'all the same' and can't be trusted to tackle climate change. And they talk about cost: the sheer expense of transforming a world built on fossil-fuel emissions into a green society.

My team and I certainly haven't solved these problems – if we had, I suspect I'd have won even more votes in 2021. But we have come up with a few fixes that worked for us, and might work for others too. Beating apathy by convincing voters that we're not just experiencing a climate crisis, but a health crisis too. Taking on cynicism by building coalitions with people from across the political spectrum. And tackling the cost of the green transition by ensuring that the burden is shared equitably across the whole of society.

So I've organised this book around the seven biggest problems we've encountered in tackling the climate crisis. Each chapter introduces a different obstacle, and explains how we tried to overcome it. I might have called the book 'The Seven Obstacles to Effective Climate Policy, and How to Surmount Them' – except with a title that dry, I suspect you wouldn't be reading this now.

More than anything, I want this book to offer a message of hope to anyone feeling helpless about climate change. Because it isn't too late: the climate crisis is ours to avert.

In the end, that insight was the one positive outcome of my London Marathon experience. On the face of it, the whole thing was a political disaster. The *Evening Standard* endorsed Tessa Jowell, not me, as the Labour candidate for Mayor. Then they backed Zac Goldsmith, not me, in the mayoral election. Also, I got asthma.

But then look at what it taught me. I learned that climate change is a force that harms all of us – not people 'over there' in the distant future, but Londoners, right here and right now. I learned that nothing feels as good as improving the environment of the city you love. And I learned that London is filled with brilliant, thoughtful, motivated people who want to do their bit. People like Rosamund.

Seven years since we first met, Rosamund remains a fearsome campaigner. She's got a knack for keeping me on my toes. In 2021, on one of my regular phone-in shows on LBC radio, she called in to request that I expand the ULEZ to all of London. She's addressed global audiences from the United Nations to the international COP26 climate conference in Glasgow.

Rosamund's tenacity is formidable, and I'm proud to know her as a campaigner, a Londoner, and a friend. But first and foremost, she was a mum to Ella.

For me, Ella humanised why the environment matters. Her short life forced people to face up to the invisible killer that we all breathe every day.

Ella shows that the climate emergency we face is a health crisis too. Ella shows why we cannot wait to take action to clean up our air.

That is why we keep going, further and faster. For Ella.

Obstacle 1
Fatalism

The conference wasn't what I had expected at all.

Where I had pictured a glamorous Parisian building a little like the Louvre, we appeared to be meeting in a glorified aircraft hangar populated by pop-up desks. And while I had envisaged hobnobbing along the Champs-Elysées, the world's leaders had actually descended on an unassuming suburb a 45-minute Métro ride from the city centre. If it weren't for all the politicians wandering from room to room, you'd never have guessed this was one of the most important climate events in modern history.

I had travelled across the Channel to attend COP21, the United Nations' landmark climate change conference in December 2015. Representatives from almost 200 countries were coming together to negotiate what would become the Paris Agreement – a legally binding international treaty to limit global warming to well below 2°C. It was an event for A-list politicians and A*-list celebrities, with everyone from President Barack Obama to Sean Penn in attendance. Unfortunately, I was not in that number. I was not visiting as mayor, nor even as an MP – but as Labour's mayoral candidate for the forthcoming mayoral election in London. Most of the attendees had no idea who I was.

But if I was underwhelmed by the not-quite-Versailles in which the conference was taking place – and disappointed that I hadn't managed to sit down with the Mayor of Bruges, let alone Sean Penn – I knew it didn't really matter. I wasn't there for the architecture, nor even the celebrities. In fact, most people in Britain had never even heard of the person I was in Paris to meet: Anne Hidalgo.

Anne had been sworn in as the Mayor of Paris the previous April, and was an inspiration. Even just a few months into her term, she was a walking refutation of one of the most widespread truisms about climate politics. People think politicians are impotent when it comes to climate. What can any one administration really do about a problem so massive? This assumption is especially true of municipal government. Climate change is a global problem, people think. What good can the mayor of a city do?

Anne was a one-woman proof this worldview was nonsense. She had been elected on a platform that included improving and extending public transport, increasing green space, and closing the city to diesel vehicles by 2020. And in the months since taking office, she had developed plans for *Paris Respire* ('Paris Breathes'), which included banning all cars from certain areas of the city on the first Sunday of the month. Even here in Paris, at the heart of an international climate conference, people remained pessimistic about whether the climate challenge could actually be overcome. But in defiance of the depressing grey walls of our meeting room in the bowels of the conference centre, Anne's enthusiasm was infectious. She spoke passionately about her campaign, her green policies, and her plans to reduce car use to 'give Paris back to Parisians'.

I left the meeting buzzing with excitement. It turned out Anne and I had a great deal in common: she was also the child of immigrants, and during our conversation we had discovered that both of our mums had worked as seamstresses. But I wasn't just interested in Anne's story for its own sake. I was interested because of what her story might mean for London. Because less than six months after our meeting, it would be the 2016 London mayoral election. I too would be standing as a centre-left politician in a global megacity. And my team and I were just starting to work out how we intended to win.

Not many people know this, but my dad was a London bus driver. One of my earliest memories is sitting at the front of the top deck of the 44 bus with my brother Tariq, as my dad drove north from Tooting up to Battersea and across the River Thames. In those pre-CCTV days, the driver would see what was happening on the top deck by peering up a periscope which showed a mirror view of the passengers on the floor above. Tariq and I would spend half the time pretending to drive, and half peering through the periscope at our dad below, laughing every time he looked up and caught us. When the bus reached its destination at Victoria, we'd run down the steps and join him for a quick cup of tea before heading back up the stairs for the return journey.

When we were a bit older, we'd pay 60p for a Red Rover ticket that would allow us to travel across the whole of London. Me and my siblings' favourite trick was to jump off the back of the Routemaster buses at the traffic lights when one of us (usually my younger brother Khaliq) least expected it, leaving them stuck on the bus as it drove off into the distance.

These early years on the buses marked the beginning of my love affair with Tooting, and with London. My political career has been motivated as much by my infatuation with this strange, unique, enormous city as by my love of politics itself. I began my career as a lawyer. I loved the job, particularly when I got to the stage where I was helping run the firm, Christian Khan: winning a good case meant you could improve people's lives, and when you won a ground-breaking case you could raise awareness about an important issue. 'Why would anyone leave a career like that behind?' my mum often asked me.

The answer, of course, was Tooting. I have adored this place for as long as I can remember. It isn't just where I was born, grew up, married, had children and now live. It is who I am. So when, in 2004, I was given an opportunity to stand as MP for Tooting, I didn't hesitate. I had been a member of the Labour Party since I was 15, and a councillor in Tooting since I was 23. When Tom Cox, who had been the local MP since 1970 – literally my entire life – announced he was standing down, I put everything into securing the candidacy.

Being elected as the MP for Tooting on 5 May 2005 was one of the best days of my life. The fact that this community – the place my parents had chosen to call home after emigrating from Pakistan – had picked me as their MP was a huge source of pride to my mum. I was just gutted that my dad wasn't there to see it. He had passed away 18 months before the 2005 general election, within a month of being diagnosed with an aggressive form of pancreatic cancer. It wasn't until a while after my election that I was informed I was the first ever London MP of Islamic faith to be elected. My dad would have loved that.

It was an exciting time to become a new Labour MP. The party had just won another five years in government, and I had the chance to be part of that – getting particularly involved in the debate over Labour's anti-terror policies, where I led the opposition to detaining people for 90 days without charge (not the best way to ingratiate myself with the party whips, I soon discovered). But even as I became increasingly involved in national politics, I found myself getting more and more interested in my home city. Two months after I was first elected as an MP, on 7 July 2005, London suffered a horrific terrorist attack that killed 52 people and injured hundreds more. I spent all morning ringing Saadiya, family and friends to check if they were okay: most of them had used the Tube or caught a bus that morning. In a strange way, that horrific day made me love London more. It revealed the resilience and solidarity between all Londoners. I remember seeing people from all walks of life and all faiths helping each other get through the days that followed. We were one.

At the same time, I was starting to chafe against the constraints of national politics. Parliament had a conspicuous culture of 'staying in your lane'. Stray outside your lane – which, as a junior minister, was a pretty narrow one – and you could quickly become unpopular with the people in charge. In government you had to accept the front-bench decision or quit: this was what 'collective responsibility' meant. I was constantly having to curtail my opinions, and, at times, argue points of view that I didn't actually support. I was yearning to do my own thing.

By the early 2010s, with Labour back in opposition, my colleagues had started to take notice. In 2013, the Labour leader Ed Miliband appointed me shadow minister for London, in addition to my existing role as shadow justice secretary. This lane was much less narrow. For the first time, my brief covered everything – from housing to transport to policing – provided it had something to do with the capital. Soon afterwards, a huge political map of London – colour-coded by borough – went up on the wall of my Westminster office. I knew then that this city was going to be the focus of my career.

There was just one problem. In the eyes of many politicians, UK politics has a very clear hierarchy: government ministers at the top, followed by MPs, with regional or 'local' representatives a distant third. Why would anyone want to give up a seat in the Palace of Westminster for an office in City Hall?

The issue, my colleagues said, was the constitution. The UK has an unusually centralised political system, in which a massive amount of power resides in Westminster. Unlike most of Europe, three-quarters of UK public expenditure is directly controlled by the government (compared to, say, 20 per cent in Germany).[1] And so, the theory goes, almost all important decisions are made by central government.

I didn't agree with this interpretation. But, to be fair, the existing government of London hadn't done much to dispel it. In 2010, the Conservative-led government had begun a programme of austerity, implementing huge cuts to public services. A policy that the mayor, Boris Johnson, had avidly supported. He wrote that the government should 'bear down on wasteful public spending',[2] and made little effort to limit the cuts across London. The mayoralty's focus had shifted away from building homes for social rent and neighbourhood policing, and towards big-ticket items that had little impact on the lives of Londoners: cable cars, a garden bridge, and two unusable water cannons following the 2011 riots. It was difficult to quantify how Londoners benefited from having a mayor at all.

If that was true in general, it was particularly true when it came to climate change. When Boris Johnson had taken over City Hall from Ken Livingstone in 2008, he inherited a city that was leading the world with innovative environmental policies and programmes: from the Congestion Charge on vehicles entering Central London, to the Oyster card that revolutionised the ease of using public transport. Fast-forward a decade, and these efforts had ground to a halt – in some areas, we had gone backwards. Within months of being elected, Johnson had abandoned the extension of the Congestion Charge zone, telling the public, incorrectly, that 'the effect on both pollution and congestion, we think, will be vanishingly small' – at the same time using his lucrative columns in the *Telegraph* to mock 'eco-doomsters' and describe concerns about climate change as a 'primitive fear without foundation'.[3]

How had he got away with it? The answer might be that people had simply given up on politicians altogether. The despairing, catastrophic messaging around climate change makes people think it is an insurmountable challenge. This is a boon to politicians like Boris Johnson: people neither expect nor hope they will take tough action. In the run-up to the 2015 Paris conference, just 19 per cent of Britons thought that a deal would be reached at all; even today, 60 per cent of the British public doesn't think the UK will hit its climate commitments by 2050.[4] This outlook can often slip into fatalism. In one poll of citizens in 27 countries, less than 30 per cent of people said they believed that government would take the lead on climate change – with a fifth of young people saying they believed it was 'too late' to fix climate change at all.[5] In a perverse way, this fatalistic outlook lets politicians off the hook. If we're going to miss our targets regardless, then why bother doing anything at all?

The received wisdom seemed to be that nobody could really do anything about climate change – and even if anyone could try, it certainly wasn't going to be the mayor. It was a profoundly depressing worldview, yet one that seemed to have become deeply embedded in the public imagination. But for me, this problem was also an opportunity. Because, by 2014, I was starting to settle on a new ambition. I was going to run as Labour's candidate for Mayor of London. And I was going to show that, when it came to climate, politicians were anything but impotent.

In November 2014, a book called *If Mayors Ruled the World* dropped through my letterbox. Its author, Benjamin R. Barber, was an American political theorist and one of the world's best-known analysts of democracy. I had bought a copy at the recommendation of a friend, who said its argument might chime with my growing interest in London's politics.

Barber's argument had two strands.[6] His first was that national politics is both dysfunctional and declining in importance. All the major challenges we face – from security to immigration to climate change – demand collaboration across borders. Yet while international bodies like the United Nations and G20 have been effective in brokering agreements, time and again national governments have proved themselves incapable of taking the action needed to implement them.

Step forward, cities. Barber's second point was that cities are on the rise, proving remarkably adept at filling the gaps left by the failures of national governments. The best mayors, Barber said, tend to have a 'preference for pragmatism and problem-solving over ideology'.[7] They often don't have much choice in the matter: mayors must deal with the unyielding, day-to-day challenge of keeping their communities afloat. As the former Mayor of Philadelphia Michael Nutter put it during a US government shutdown – in which many federal services stop running due to a dispute over budgets – 'Mayors could never get away with the kind of nonsense that goes on in Washington. In our world, you either picked up the trash or you didn't . . . That's what we do every day. And we know how to get this stuff done.'[8]

As such, municipal leaders are often well-liked and

trusted by citizens. Recent polling across 22 countries in the developed world, including the UK, shows far higher levels of trust in local than in national government.[9] My main takeaway from Barber's book was that, while mayors don't quite 'rule the world', they certainly rule much of it – with more than half of the world's population living in cities, and that number likely rising to two-thirds by 2050. Above all, I liked the book's countless anecdotes about how mayors were rising to the biggest challenges facing the planet. Page after page featured stories of mayors acting outside the narrow confines of national party politics: from Leoluca Orlando of Palermo seeing crime rates reverse after confronting the local Mafia, to Teddy Kollek of Jerusalem ably traversing the conflicts surrounding access to religious sites.

In the days after I read Barber's book, I couldn't stop thinking about what his argument might mean for London. With a budget of almost £20 billion and wide-ranging powers over transport, policing and regeneration, City Hall has a unique role in shaping the city. The mayor controls Transport for London (TfL), which runs the capital's public transport, operates the Congestion Charge, and oversees many of the main roads and cycle lanes. The mayor is London's police and crime commissioner, over-seeing police spending and the capital's policing strategy. And that's not to mention the mayor's oversight of housing strategy, the London Fire Brigade, and various aspects of city regeneration. For eight years under Boris Johnson, many of these levers had barely been touched. But they were there, ready for any mayor ambitious enough to take hold of them.

That Christmas there was feverish speculation about who would stand to be the next Mayor of London. I'd been pondering standing as Labour's candidate for months. Not everyone was supportive. Since being elected on the same day in 2005, my fellow London Labour MP Dawn Butler had become not only a close confidant, but one of my best friends – and she was adamant that I should stay in Parliament. On the other hand, another London Labour colleague and friend, Karen Buck MP, could see the difference a Labour mayor in City Hall could make to her constituents. Armed with Barber's analysis of how mayors were changing the world, I felt more drawn to the mayoral race than ever. My sense that London's politics was my calling was bolstered by the results of the 2015 general election. On an otherwise disappointing night for Labour across the country, we gained seven parliamentary seats in London, our strongest performance since 2001. Labour in London did far better than in the UK overall, achieving 43.7 per cent of the vote – an increase of over seven points on 2010. After eight years of a Conservative mayor, City Hall was within Labour's grasp.

My team and I launched my campaign to secure the candidacy a week later, at the Anchor Church in Earlsfield – a stone's throw from the council estate where I grew up. This was a whole different ball game to my campaign to be the Labour candidate for Tooting. Suddenly, I was at the epicentre of a massive team of volunteers – much bigger than anything I'd experienced before. We rented a set of basic rooms in Whitechapel, which became our selection campaign HQ. Time and money were tight. The windows of the office wouldn't open, and the kitchen was infested with vermin. One of the mice that scurried around the room became our de facto mascot. We called him Boris.

But what we lacked in vermin-free office space, we made up for with the passion of our volunteers. One of them, Mete Coban, soon came up with a catchy, Barack Obama-inspired slogan: #YesWeKhan. Yet even armed with a self-aggrandisingly presidential slogan and the support of Boris the office mouse, we had a hell of a campaign ahead of us. First, I needed the Labour Party to select me as their candidate. Not easy. In a poll conducted by the *Guardian* in March 2015, I had come fifth among a list of potential runners and riders – behind Alan Johnson (who ultimately didn't run) and Diane Abbott, Tessa Jowell and David Lammy (who all did).[10]

I decided the solution was to speak to as many London Labour members and supporters as I could. The party had just implemented a new primary system which meant you didn't need to be a member to vote, just pay a small one-off fee to register as a supporter. Everyone, from the newest 16-year-old supporter to the most veteran MP, was given an equal say. Over the next four months, I made over 200 visits to workplaces, community centres, bus garages, churches, temples, mosques and shopping malls to attract new supporters; Dawn joined me on many of them. Visits in South-West London were particularly enjoyable. At a bus garage in Putney, several drivers I met claimed to have worked with my dad, which was lovely – even if some of them turned out to only have begun driving in the mid-1990s, long after he had retired.

On 11 September 2015, the candidates – Tessa Jowell MP, David Lammy MP, Diane Abbott MP, Gareth Thomas MP, transport expert Christian Wolmar and I – descended on the Southbank Centre, along with our teams. It had been a hard-fought campaign, and my nerves were shot. They only got worse when I saw Jack Stenner, by now my political director, dressed in a suit and tie for the first time in years. Clearly this was serious business.

The other candidates had assumed a close but clear victory, and not for us. Right up until the moment of the announcement, my team were being congratulated, in a mildly patronising manner, for doing a 'really good job'. Someone even questioned whether it was wise for Saadiya to be sitting in the front row, given their expectation that I was set to lose.

As the results were read out, I held on to Saadiya's hand for dear life. In the final round of voting, Tessa had won 33,573 votes. I had won 48,152.

We had done it. I had won the candidacy. With 59 per cent of the vote.

I was euphoric. To this day, I have no idea what I said in my victory speech – all I remember is the electric atmosphere and the whoops and cheers of my campaign team. But there was no time to rest. Within hours, I was back on the campaign trail, this time with the assistance of the London Labour regional team, who were now working for me in my capacity as the official candidate. The maps of London that had once been so integral to my campaigns were now less relevant. By this point, I knew London's boroughs and constituencies like the back of my hand – and rather than take a borough-by-borough approach we had decided that I was going to compete for every vote in the city, from the leafiest Tory suburb to the most consistently Labour inner-city neighbourhoods.

We just had to come up with a platform. Now, don't get me wrong – I love the Labour Party. But anyone who has ever been involved in writing a manifesto will know that it is a total nightmare. The manifesto-drafting process involves consulting everyone and everything. As a result, you often end up with a grab-bag of policies that appeals to everyone in the party, and not nearly enough people outside of it. We were determined not to do that. Overall, our campaign was going to home in on the areas where the mayor could make the biggest difference – an approach inspired, in part, by Benjamin Barber. Ours was the first Labour mayoral manifesto to feature an entire chapter devoted to the environment – involving 33 pledges that ranged from making London the world's first 'National Park City', to introducing cleaner vehicles and rolling out new cycle lanes, to planting thousands more trees and divesting London's pensions fund from fossil fuel investments. Most importantly of all, we pledged to clean up London's toxic air. And we had designed the whole package to ensure any costs were shared equitably, with the best-off shouldering most of the burden.

In short, I wanted to be a green mayor. There was just one problem. So did my main opponent.

In October, we had learned the Conservative candidate for Mayor of London was Zac Goldsmith. He was a politician with a strong interest in green issues. His uncle, Edward Goldsmith, had been an early pioneer of the green movement – founding the *Ecologist* magazine, which Zac later edited, and setting up the first green political party, People, which later became the Green Party. Early in the campaign Zac shared a fantastic story about his uncle touring East Anglia with a camel, campaigning under the slogan 'No deserts in Suffolk'. He was accused of animal cruelty because of the impact the car fumes might have on the camel. 'That's exactly my point,' he replied. 'Imagine what it's doing to us!'

Zac Goldsmith's selection was a worrying development. On the face of it, he seemed like the one Conservative politician who could out-green us. He had been brought in by the Conservative leader David Cameron to 'detoxify' the Tory brand, and had form in cutting across political divides. In the 2010 general election, he had defeated the Liberal Democrats in Richmond Park to become the MP with a 7 per cent swing in his favour, and in the 2015 general election he increased his majority from 4,000 to 23,000 votes: the biggest increase in majority of any MP. He also seemed like a nice guy.

On the night we discovered Goldsmith was going to be our rival, the atmosphere in the office was tense. We thought it meant 2016 was going to be a 'green' election – in which many of the most important battles would be fought over environmental policy. I decided I wanted to go head-to-head with Goldsmith on his strengths – like environment – rather than those where I had a lot of support already – like housing and transport. It was our only hope of neutralising the threat that his green credentials posed.

But on the campaign trail, nothing unfolded quite as we had expected. The first of what was to be many mayoral debates took place in January 2016 at the London School of Economics. But while we talked through other areas – like housing and transport – in detail, whenever the environment came up the debate never really got off the ground. Goldsmith seemed to shy away from making bold commitments. The discussion centred largely around relatively uncontroversial pledges like not building on the green belt, and introducing pollution limits.

My team and I were confused. This was a 'green' Tory candidate fighting in a 'green' city. Yet 'greenness' didn't seem to be something that Goldsmith wanted to talk about. It was a pattern that would repeat again and again in the months that followed. While I enjoyed campaigning alongside the Greens' Siân Berry and Lib Dems' Caroline Pidgeon – and learned a lot from them both – with Zac Goldsmith most of our attempts to talk about green issues fell flat. It was a confusing strategy. The Labour campaign team had put many hours into understanding Goldsmith's environmental credentials, which we thought posed a major threat – and yet, in the campaign itself, he didn't seem to want to discuss them.

I came to wonder if Goldsmith had simply accepted the received wisdom about mayors. Climate change, we had all been told, wasn't something politicians could solve. It was too big a challenge for any one candidate, whether the prime minister or the mayor. In particular, City Hall could do little about it. And so Goldsmith had apparently chosen to dodge environmental policy altogether.

As the election campaign wore on, and our poll lead grew, Goldsmith seemed to get less interested in policy, green or otherwise – and more interested in dog-whistles. He hired a firm co-founded by the infamous Australian election and political strategist Sir Lynton Crosby to run his mayoral campaign. I was accused of being 'dangerous' and 'a radical'. In a particularly surreal moment, the Goldsmith campaign wrote to British Indians claiming that I supported a wealth tax on their family jewellery. I kept trying to strike an upbeat tone and focus on the policy, but the mood on the campaign trail was often depressing. The nadir was when Goldsmith wrote an article in the *Mail on Sunday* four days before the election, headlined 'Are we really going to hand the world's greatest city to a Labour party that thinks terrorists is its friends? [*sic*]' – and illustrated by a picture of a bus destroyed in the 7/7 attacks.[11] I wasn't the only person who wondered whether such an attack line would have been used against a candidate who wasn't of Islamic faith. At one point in the campaign I ended up tweeting, 'Hey @ZacGoldsmith. There's no need to keep pointing at me & shouting "he's a Muslim". I put it on my own leaflets.'

As election night approached, it started to feel like Goldsmith and I had both placed a bet. Mine was on policy: informed by a belief that politicians really could change the world, even on issues as big as the environment.

Goldsmith's was on personality: a tactic that had led him to a series of increasingly outrageous innuendos about my background and politics.

The only thing left to find out was whose gamble would pay off.

*

The Mayor of London's headquarters was usually a tranquil place. Located just next to Tower Bridge, the building tended to be surrounded by tourists ambling along the south bank of the Thames. But on the afternoon of 7 May 2016, it was packed. As Saadiya and I walked towards the building for the mayoral results announcement, a member of my team told me it was 'quite busy'. A slight understatement. As soon as we were spotted by the press, photographers swarmed us. We could barely move. I clutched Saadiya's hand, desperately trying to prevent us getting separated as we forced our way through the final 30 metres to the doors of City Hall. Amid the chaos, two members of my campaign team were photographed and subsequently captioned as my daughters on the front page of *The Times*.

Eventually we made it through the front doors and up to the seventh floor of City Hall, where the Labour Party London Assembly Members were based, to wait for the expected 5pm announcement. I was anxious. For at least four months now, the polls had shown me ahead of Goldsmith – but most people in the Labour Party knew better than to trust polls, particularly when up against a very negative Tory campaign. Only the previous year, pollsters had been predicting that Ed Miliband would become prime minister at the general election, only for Labour to experience a crushing defeat at the hands of David Cameron. Truth be told, Labour hadn't won any big elections since 2005.

Unfortunately for my anxiety levels, mayoral and London Assembly counts are also notoriously slow. In 2012, polls had closed at 10pm on 3 May and results weren't announced until just before midnight the following day. To keep myself distracted, I spent the evening writing and amending my victory speech. But as the minutes turned into hours, I realised I could well be nervously rewriting my speech for days. Shortly before 5pm, a City Hall official appeared and asked everyone to head down to the chamber on the second floor for the results. Everyone else set off, leaving me to tensely read through my speech one final time and eat my emergency Snickers bar. Five minutes later, just as I began to head down, everyone else tramped back upstairs. It had been a false alarm. My emergency Snickers, wasted.

Fast-forward five hours, and we were still waiting. The mood had transitioned from excited to tense to hungry. Everything was going off the rails. The team had sent out distress signals and someone's sister had ordered pizzas to City Hall; they had caused a huge fuss because the security team insisted on putting them through the X-ray machine. I was getting updates that at my campaign party a few minutes' walk away, my friends and campaign team were getting progressively drunker: one member of the team had persuaded Bill Bailey to do an impromptu comedy set. On the plus side, the wait was doing wonders for inter-party relations. Caroline, the Liberal Democrat candidate and Assembly Member, kindly took my two extremely bored daughters, Anisah and Ammarah, on a private tour of City Hall.

At half past midnight, ten hours after we'd arrived – and after more false alarms – word reached us that the count was finally finished. I headed down to the City Hall chamber for one of the most nerve-wracking moments of my career. It was my first time ever in the chamber, and I was immediately struck by the architecture. The elaborate spiral staircase leads right up from the chamber to the top floor of the building, where the mayor's office is located. I was honoured to be standing alongside many of my fellow candidates, particularly Siân and Caroline, with whom I had become friendly. In contrast, Zac Goldsmith refused to shake my hand after the result, and the candidate for Britain First – the far-right, racist political party – turned his back on me.

I was feeling on edge. But it never fails to amaze me how in a crowd you can always pick out the voices of the people you know – and as soon as I heard the claps and whoops from Anisah and Ammarah I felt better.

And I felt better again when the results were read out. I had been elected – and with the highest number and share of first-preference votes since mayoral elections had begun.

It was a victory for hope over fear, and unity over division. But above all, it was a vote of confidence in the power of individual politicians to make a difference. For years, Londoners had been told politicians couldn't do anything of substance on the big issues – housing, education, and, above all, the climate. But London had realised that actually, they could. The world's problems were the mayor's problems.

Six hours later, as I walked into my new office on the eighth floor of City Hall, I had to laugh. There wasn't a map of London's 32 boroughs or of the 73 parliamentary constituencies, like we'd had in my Westminster office. But an entire wall of the mayor's office was taken up with a map that showed every single street of the city. Time to get to work.

Obstacle 2

Apathy

Sir John Cass's Foundation Primary was the kind of school that could only exist in London.

Located just inside the ancient east gate of the City of London, it was nestled snugly between some of the country's most remarkable buildings – a fragment of Roman city wall here, a medieval church there, and the Gherkin towering over everything from a few metres to the north-west. It was the sort of school that parents boast of sending their kids to: a brilliant state primary, open to everyone, in the vibrant heart of the world's greatest city.

In fact, everything about Sir John Cass was exemplary except the air quality.

Just a few metres from the school was the A11, one of the busiest thoroughfares running from the City into East London. Inside the school was the constant roar of traffic; outside, the air felt suffocating. You could almost taste the pollution.

On Friday 13 May 2016, less than a week after my election as Mayor of London, I paid a visit to Sir John Cass. In defiance of its polluted surroundings, the school had begun several environmental initiatives – including creating a green roof garden to help teach pupils about the natural world. That's why we were there. Where better place to announce that we'd be launching the biggest public consultation and education programme on air quality in London's history?

These were early days in my mayoralty, and we were still finding our feet. Upon arriving at the school, I met with the teachers and students to discuss my plans while helping out with some weeding. About an hour into the day, I heard some alarmed mutterings coming from my team behind me. They had spotted that I had forgotten to wear my wedding ring. Normally this wouldn't have worried anyone – but given who I'd just succeeded as mayor, and his reputation for infidelity, they didn't want to take any chances. In the end, the journalists present didn't notice my jewellery mishap, but they were bemused by the trip. Reporters kept asking my team why I'd chosen the school as my first proper mayoral visit.

Our reasoning was simple. During the election campaign, we had often found it difficult to get coverage of our climate policies. Hustings events, where candidates come together to debate policies and address potential voters, had taken place across the city on topics from transport to housing – and were usually religiously attended by the London and national media. But there were far fewer climate-focused events, and those there were attracted little media attention.

The assumption seemed to be that climate change was something that happened 'over there'. The term conjured up images of rising sea levels in Bangladesh, or desertification in East Africa. A problem, certainly. But not one that anyone in London needed to pay much heed to.

Sir John Cass's Foundation Primary School proved otherwise. The climate crisis was an issue right here in London.

Making Sir John Cass the first proper mayoral visit was our attempt to force the media to notice. As I argued in my remarks at the school, we had been here before. In previous air crises London had only responded *after* the emergency. The vast Victorian sewers were only constructed after the Great Stink in 1858; the Clean Air Act followed the Great Smog of London of the 1950s. Now, it was happening again. Since 2010, the government had been hopelessly inactive on air quality and it was the most vulnerable Londoners who would suffer as a result. This time, I wanted to act *before* the emergency.

The trick was getting people to understand the scale of the problem. Unlike the Great Smog (or the Great Stink), you couldn't actually see (or smell) the toxicity in the air in 2016. It was an invisible killer, and that made the task of raising awareness much harder. During my first 100 days in office, I was repeatedly told that Londoners – and Britons – just weren't that interested in green issues. I was told that people wanted green policies, but the issue had low 'salience': voters consistently prioritised the environment below other, apparently more pressing, issues. Polling undertaken a few months into my mayoralty showed that housing, transport and protecting jobs were far higher priorities for Londoners. Of those questioned, twice the number chose building genuinely affordable homes over tackling air pollution.[1]

The only way to turn the tide on climate, my team thought, was to demonstrate that climate change wasn't just something happening 'over there'. It was affecting every Londoner, every day. It was disproportionately harming the worst-off members of our community. And with every polluting vehicle that drove through London, it was getting worse.

My most vivid memory from the days after election night is of Southwark Cathedral. I recall walking, dazed, through the throngs of people who had come to the ceremony in which I accepted the mayoralty. We had been planning the event for weeks: instead of a boringly administrative 'sign-in' at City Hall, we wanted an interfaith ceremony that brought together Londoners of all religions and backgrounds. We were pleased to see such a diverse crowd, but I was temporarily startled by just how diverse: suddenly, to my mild alarm, Gandalf the Grey's face loomed forward out of the crowd. It took a few seconds for my sleep-deprived brain to piece together that we weren't, in fact, in an unusually crowded version of the Shire; just that Sir Ian McKellen had come to offer his support.

This moment marked the nadir of my tired brain's increasingly muddled attempts to make sense of what was going on in the days after my election. My victory had been announced at half past midnight, and in the next few hours I'd barely slept – there had been too much adrenaline coursing through my veins. That set the tone for the hectic week that followed. Your first few days as mayor are intense, and often surreal.

My first goal was to make sure I was well equipped to protect the people of London from harm. So I commissioned a review of all London's counter-terrorism measures. This meant that shortly after my election I spent a morning taking part in a simulation of a marauding terrorist attack. Early in the morning, I arrived in a characterless building near Tower Bridge, where I was met by Sir Bernard Hogan-Howe, the metropolitan police commissioner. We were escorted into a large area designed to mimic the basic layout of a shopping centre. Within moments a group of men burst in with guns, taking fire at the 'shoppers' perusing the shelves. As the (fake) bodies piled up and the area filled with smoke, Sir Bernard talked me through the emergency services' response. Even though we knew it was a simulation, the minutes spent waiting for the police, ambulance and fire services to arrive felt like an eternity. It was terrifying, but I gained a small glimpse into what it would be like to be caught up in a terror attack.

But I also knew that protecting Londoners from harm

goes way beyond policing. One of my first priorities was to tackle the air-quality crisis. Easier said than done, I soon discovered. The obstacles were varied. First of all, it seemed that the previous administration had pretty much given up on convincing Londoners to worry about air pollution. If the public didn't care, the previous mayor seemed to have concluded, then there was no reason he should care either.

The effects of this worldview led to problems that rippled across City Hall. First, it led to the underuse of the mayor's resources. One of the most surprising things about the City Hall I inherited was the sheer number of extremely talented employees, many of whom had largely been left to their own devices over the previous eight years. Everyone knew that Boris Johnson had been a hands-off mayor. But I was shocked by just how little use had been made of the impressive staff who worked for the mayoralty. The environment team were one such example; a group who for some time had been reliant on their own initiative to progress an agenda that had largely been ignored. When I appointed the City Hall veteran Shirley Rodrigues as my Deputy Mayor for Environment and Energy a few months after my election, she reassured us about what we'd already discovered: there were some great people in the team – just they had been under-stretched for years.

I was lucky to have a top team in my chief of staff, David Bellamy, my mayoral directors, Nick Bowes, Paddy

Hennessy and Leah Kreitzman – and of course Jack and Ali. We set about trying to make proper use of the City Hall staff. During my selection and election campaigns we had run a daily planning meeting which brought together representatives from every part of the team, from policy to communications. This process now transferred to City Hall. For the next few years at 9.30am various team members from across the building would assemble in room 8.7 – a nondescript meeting room on the eighth floor, a few metres from my office, that would become the unassuming heart of mayoral strategy. The environment team became a key part of this operation. Shirley would sometimes take the opportunity to tell us about the status of the beloved spider plant on her desk, which soon became our environmental mascot. Over the years, various members of my team would cut off the baby spider plants and propagate them, until the striped green leaves could soon be found sprouting in all areas of City Hall.

The systemic underuse of the City Hall machine led on to a second problem: a lack of accurate, publicly available information about London, and particularly about the environment. The issue wasn't so much that City Hall didn't have good data to hand; rather that this data sat buried in filing cabinets and hard drives. Within days of entering office, I learned that City Hall had commissioned a report by the independent air quality and climate change emissions consultancy Aether back in 2013. I was alarmed to learn about the existence of this report: how could my team have missed such an important document during my mayoral campaign? So I asked whether we should look into republishing the data. The team told me that wasn't an option. Why? Because it had never been published in the first place.

The report was damning. It revealed that hundreds of the capital's primary schools were in areas where pollution breached the EU's legal limits.[2] Of those, 83 per cent were considered 'deprived' schools where more than 40 per cent of the pupils were entitled to free school meals. In the poorest areas, half of the air was in breach of EU limits – compared to just 1 per cent of the air in the richest areas. It was the poorest Londoners – those least likely to own a car – who were suffering some of the worst consequences. City Hall had known this for years, but Londoners had never even been told.

In my first few months in office, we collected ever more damning evidence about the scale of the air-quality crisis; evidence that the previous administration could have gathered, but hadn't. During the 'Saharan Dust' episode of 2014, in which southern England was covered by a film of red dust blown over from the Sahara Desert, the London ambulance service reported a 14 per cent rise in emergency 999 calls for patients with respiratory issues, and a higher than normal volume of calls from people with breathing difficulties, asthma and heart problems. There were 49 such instances of poor air quality in 2014, and a further 48 in 2015. Subsequently we found that hundreds of primary schools and almost 100 secondary schools were experiencing air pollution levels above the legal limit every day – a total of 443 schools across the capital.[3] Sir John Cass's Foundation Primary was right at the top, with the highest level of pollution in London. Just weeks ago I'd stood on its rooftop playground telling journalists I wanted to act *before* the emergency. It turned out it was already here.

Even as a full-time politician with a personal interest, I'd had no idea about the scale of this problem. Londoners with hay fever were told in the weather forecast when the pollen count would be high and so could act appropriately – yet Londoners with serious respiratory problems had no idea at all when the air quality was bad. The government's advice was that during episodes of poor air quality, anyone with lung problems, adults with heart problems, and older people should all avoid strenuous physical activity. Yet the general public had not been privy to information about these episodes.

During the election campaign, we had often wondered why voters had seemed so apathetic about the environment. Now we were in City Hall, the answers became obvious. Because Londoners had never been told about the environmental crisis going on all around them, many of them didn't care. And this problem, I suspected, was being compounded by human psychology. My experience as both a lawyer and a politician had led me to conclude that our brains simply can't engage with the problem of climate change. Humans are wired to deal with immediate threats – the car coming towards us as we cross the road, the eviction notice giving us a month to leave a property – rather than longer-term ones like climate change. On top of that, our built-in belief that everything will be okay – the 'optimism bias' – makes us envisage a bright future despite clear evidence to the contrary. 'Many environmentalists say climate change is happening too fast,' says the psychology professor Daniel Gilbert. 'No, it's happening too slowly. It's not happening nearly quickly enough to get our attention.'[4]

All this posed a problem for my environmental ambitions. During these early days in City Hall, we realised that tackling the climate crisis wasn't just going to come down to policy making. It was going to come down to persuasion. I needed to show the city that the environment mattered. Not just in the future, on the other side of the world. Right here in London. Right now.

On 5 July 2016, almost two months to the day since my election as mayor, I walked through the door of the respiratory unit at Great Ormond Street Hospital. I was greeted by Dr Colin Wallis, a respiratory paediatric consultant. A kind yet commanding figure, Colin was helping treat several of the hospital's young patients who were living with respiratory conditions. I was there to meet some of them.

Great Ormond Street was only the latest in my string

of air-quality-focused visits across London during my first 100 days as mayor. But until I visited the hospital, the significance of air pollution never really hit home. As I walked through the wards, the effects of the environmental crisis were more visible than ever. My asthma was manageable, but for the children I met the consequences were far more serious – and in many cases life-changing. Some were outpatients and were visiting the hospital for tests or overnight sleep studies. Others were suffering from acute or chronic lung disease, or complex respiratory conditions that meant they needed support to breathe. Many were barely old enough to walk and talk. In every case, the evidence suggested these problems had been exacerbated by poor air quality in the capital.

After meeting the children, I was due to give a speech at the hospital to mark the 60th anniversary of the Clean Air Act. The legislation had made a huge difference to Londoners and had saved countless lives. My argument was simple: we were facing another pollution emergency in London and it was our turn to act.

That meant some big, ambitious policies. In an unusually bright and airy hospital room just off the respiratory ward, I outlined the measures my team were planning to tackle the pollution crisis. A £10 emissions toxicity surcharge (dubbed the 'T-Charge') on the most polluting vehicles entering Central London – a change that would come in in October 2017, 15 months later. A diesel scrappage scheme, run through TfL – which offered motorists cash rewards to part with their old, polluting cars, provided the proceeds went to a cleaner vehicle. And finally, my most significant environmental policy of all: the Central London Ultra Low Emission Zone, in which vehicles would have to meet strict emissions requirements or face a daily charge to travel. It would be a world first if introduced.

This felt like a political gamble. Many of the bemused journalists from my visit to Sir John Cass were present, and it seemed to be sinking in that I was serious. Many of them were incandescent: why was I spending so much time and effort on an issue that few of their readers or viewers cared about? The Conservative Members of the London Assembly at City Hall couldn't believe their luck. In the days that followed, they wasted no time denouncing the initiatives I'd announced.

Yet I felt we had no choice. We needed these policies because bad air quality was having a destructive impact on the lives of millions of people. And it was particularly affecting the most deprived communities: working-class and ethnic-minority Londoners were disproportionately represented on the Great Ormond Street wards. But it was clear that we had some persuading to do. This speech wasn't just important because we were unveiling some major new policies. It was important because we were trying out our new communications strategy: one designed to overcome the problem of apathy.

That strategy was simple: to show Londoners that the

environment was a problem for them already. I knew that for Londoners to support the kinds of big policies we needed, we'd have to relate the problem of air quality to their everyday concerns. I have always admired a line attributed to the Labour politician and writer, Tony Benn: 'Being a teacher is probably the most important thing you can be in politics.'[5] I wanted to find ways to teach Londoners about how climate change related to their lives.

So, starting with the Great Ormond Street speech, we began an enormous education campaign – designed to win people round across the capital. Our persuasion campaign had three components. First, we needed better information. Before we could convince Londoners that air quality mattered, we needed the data to make the case: showing them when and where air pollution struck. In my first 100 days we introduced measures to monitor London's air quality at over 100 different locations – via recorders across the city that made the data publicly available in real-time. We also launched our School and Nursery Air Quality Audits Programme, undertaken at 50 primary schools and 20 nurseries in some of the city's most polluted areas. The audits made recommendations to reduce emissions and exposure – from 'No engine idling' schemes designed to reduce emissions from the school run, to local road changes and green infrastructure interventions like 'barrier bushes' that were planted along busy roads and in playgrounds to help filter out fumes. In time, we introduced personal monitors that children could wear on their route to school: specially adapted backpacks with a built-in monitor in one of the pockets that tracked the air quality.

Second, we had to get better at alerting people when the air quality was poor. Weeks after taking office, we instructed TfL to develop a package of alerts to better inform Londoners when air quality was at dangerous levels. By August I'd announced I was introducing air-quality alerts at over 2,500 bus countdown signs and river pier signs across London, 140 road side message signs on the busiest main roads; and electronic update signs in the entrances of all 270 London Underground stations.

The day we issued our first alert warning Londoners that there was a dangerously high level of pollution in the air was memorable. Shirley and my Head of Air Quality, Elliot Treharne, had provided me with all the scientific data I required to show why we needed the alert. But given the amount of media interest, and the importance that Londoners had confidence in the process, I didn't want to risk anything going wrong. I popped upstairs to the top-floor balcony of City Hall, where I often took part in media interviews, to have a think. As soon as I got up there, and looked out over Tower Bridge and across the River Thames winding its way to Westminster, I could see the unmistakable haze of pollution starting to settle. I had no doubt that this was going to be a bad episode. So I instructed the team to 'push the button'. As it turned out, this was more than just a figure of speech: I later discovered that the alert is indeed triggered via a special button, and that day, while many of us waited with bated breath – including several journalists who were standing by a bus covered in big numbers counting down to zero – the person responsible for pushing said button had decided to go for an ill-timed tea-break. The alert was delayed by half an hour as a result – which, while not the end of the world, was mildly embarrassing.

We soon also began to publish information for Londoners about the impact of air pollution, explaining what action they could take to minimise their own exposure – including interactive air-quality maps showing the levels of air pollution in London. In time, this would lead to us funding a new partnership with King's College London to inform the public, and particularly those who are most vulnerable, about incidents of poor air quality via text.

But the most important pillar of our persuasion campaign was the third: shouting about it. For our measures to be successful, we didn't just need to monitor the air quality and publish the information. We needed to make people actually notice. Taking inspiration from campaign groups like Mums for Lungs – an organisation established in Brixton in 2017 that was playing a key role in helping to raise awareness – we began working out how to get the word out. This proved to be the most stimulating part of our conversations about air quality. The received wisdom among many politicians is that campaigning is fun, but governing is dull – defined by detail, bureaucracy and many, many (many) stakeholder meetings. As the former Governor of New York State Mario Cuomo once put it, 'You campaign in poetry: you govern in prose.'[6] I knew what he meant: I have always adored campaigns, and I can't claim to have the same passion for stakeholder meetings. But when it came to air quality, we realised we needed to govern in poetry too. Just finding the right answer to a policy question wasn't enough: you needed to engage people in your attempts to find that answer. And for that, poetry was always going to be more effective. Or, at least, my not-quite-Pulitzer-worthy version of poetry.

In practice, that poetry tended to involve waxing lyrical about air quality across countless events, posters and billboards. On one occasion, yoga mats and 'downward dogs' replaced traffic jams as the sun rose over Tower Bridge as part of our annual 'Car Free Day' celebrations. A stone's throw away, London's financial district was taken over by children racing go-karts on the traffic-less streets. But perhaps the biggest tool we had at our disposal was advertising on the Transport for London network, on which nearly three million people travel every day. We had countless meetings in City Hall about what precise form this messaging should take – it needed to be immediately eye-catching, without being offputtingly catastrophist. Our most powerful campaign would go live in 2017. In advance of launching the T-Charge, we put up adverts across London featuring stomach-churning images of everyday objects covered in black soot, including a coffee cup and a baby's bottle. I remember being physically repelled when I was first shown the images by my mayoral director Leah Kreitzman. The caption: 'If you could see London's air, you'd want to clean it too.'

As our attempts to educate the public about the air-quality crisis gained momentum, I learned something strange about campaigning while in office.

When you are on the campaign trail during an election, the end result is short-term and unambiguous. Either you win the election, or you don't. Nerve-wracking, but simple.

But now I was mayor, the campaign objectives were more nebulous. My goal was to convince the public that the environment and air quality mattered to them. There was no point at which I could say that our campaign was 'finished' – and it was often unclear how it was going. Of course, we had the odd poll (although local polls of Londoners aren't always the most accurate). But we never knew for certain whether our message was cutting through.

That meant that as our persuasion campaign got underway, I started obsessively looking for signs that things were going well (or badly). It was a peculiar process. I remember feeling bizarrely pleased when Labour council leaders and MPs started to complain that their constituents were cross about my focus on climate issues. It meant people were noticing. A similar moment came the summer I went to Frank Skinner's show at the Edinburgh Fringe. He began with the line: 'I'm really sorry for the show starting a few minutes late. It was to allow us to find a booster seat for the Mayor of London, Sadiq Khan.' Cue huge laughs and applause. But I soon forgave him making me the butt of his opening joke when he started ad-libbing about the toxic air in London throughout the show, pretending to cough and mocking me for having time to come to Edinburgh given all the changes I was making to fix the air. Cut-through!

We only really started to know the effects of the campaign in August 2016, when we received the results of our consultation. Waiting for consultation results often feels like a mini election night. You press on through the nerves and try to get on with your day-to-day business – while knowing any minute news can come in that could change everything. It's a bit like waiting for exam results. But when the results did come in, the mood in City Hall was ecstatic. Since the consultation had been formally launched at Great Ormond Street, almost 15,000 people had responded. It showed that 79 per cent of respondents wanted to receive information about when air pollution was high so they could take action to protect their health. There was even stronger support for the T-Charge on highly polluting vehicles: 81 per cent of respondents were in favour.[7] A clear majority were also in favour of introducing the Ultra Low Emission Zone – in fact, a majority even wanted to extend it beyond Central London.

We had passed the exam then. In a few short months we'd exposed the reality of London's filthy air, and had won Londoners round to taking action. For me, the lesson was simple. Politicians had been taking the wrong insights from all those depressing polls on public attitudes to climate change. For all we'd been told that this was a 'low-salience' issue, people could be made to care about the environment. And they cared about it not in the abstract – in the form of numbers on a spreadsheet, or complex models of the climate in 2050 – but when you showed that it mattered to them here and now. The climate crisis, we had shown, was happening in the streets they walked, the parks their children played in – and the air they breathed.

A few summers later, I would be invited by James O'Brien, an LBC presenter who regularly grilled me on his daily radio show, to visit his local primary school as a guest for the summer fair. The school, St Mary's Primary, was located next to the A4 in Chiswick. Shirley Rodrigues told me the school had been one of the first to benefit from City Hall's new environmental policies and funding. It had built a 400-foot living wall, the longest in the UK, showcasing more than 12,000 plants along the perimeter of the playground. She suggested we go along to take a look.

Led by a proud dad, Andrea Carnevali, the school's parents, staff, governors and children took great pleasure in showing me the new plants on the wall, the new greenery and garden. The garden was beautiful: a small urban oasis that would eventually be open to members of the public as well as the students. I was invited to add a plant myself. Tribal as ever, I adorned my plant with a red label, signed with my name. Andrea chastised me – 'We don't do party politics here!' – and encouraged me to add a second plant with a blue label. Meanwhile, inside the classrooms, filtration systems had been installed to improve the air quality. There was even high-tech Airlite paint on the walls, which purified the air by neutralising pollutants and harmful chemicals.

As I walked from classroom to classroom, I reflected on how far we'd come since that first visit to Sir John Cass. These kids got it, and their parents and teachers got it too. The climate crisis was a health crisis, and one that was happening right now. But it was a crisis we could tackle, and we would. If we could improve the air right next to the A4 in West London, there was nowhere we couldn't make a difference.

Obstacle 3

Cynicism

As I sat in my office on the eighth floor of City Hall, I could hear the conversation outside the open door getting more and more heated.

'Don't be ridiculous. He can't possibly shake their hands.'

'Well, he can't *not* shake their hands, can he? Anyway, isn't there something you can buy to dissolve Super Glue these days? Can we get some in time?'

The date was 29 April 2019, and London was in the throes of a major wave of protests by Extinction Rebellion. Over the previous few months, XR had made headlines with a series of increasingly audacious stunts designed to raise awareness about climate change. Their first weeks of action in November 2018 had seen thousands of people take to the streets and bridges of London, and led to nearly 100 arrests. By April 2019, this had escalated to a full-scale occupation of five locations across London: Piccadilly Circus, Oxford Circus, Waterloo Bridge, Parliament Square and Marble Arch. April also brought the arrival of a pink boat, named after the murdered Honduran environmental activist Berta Cáceres and emblazoned with the phrase 'Tell the Truth'. Protesters remained continuously at these sites for nearly a week, locking themselves onto trucks (and boats) en masse. Ultimately, more than 1,100 people would be arrested over ten days.

Now, some members of XR were coming to City Hall. From day one, I'd realised that XR were capturing people's imaginations. I shared their goal, tackling the apathy many Londoners felt towards climate change. And so I wanted to talk things over. So, against the counsel of some of my senior advisors, I had asked my team to invite them into City Hall.

What I had thought was a simple ask had turned out to be unexpectedly complicated. XR have an unusual, non-hierarchical structure – so it took a little time to work out who were the appropriate members to meet with in the first place. My office eventually arranged for me to see Farhana Yamin, a leading international environmental lawyer plus climate change and development policy expert; Sam Knights, an actor, writer and XR political strategy activist; and Skeena Rathor, a Labour councillor in Stroud.

Even when faced with such an impressive group of activists, my private office and protection team were understandably apprehensive. XR were known as being an anarchic bunch, and in recent weeks members had taken to gluing and chaining themselves to buildings to cause maximum disruption. Just a few days previously, some activists had Super-Glued themselves to the two revolving doors at the front entrance of City Hall. Shortly before our meeting, we learned that Farhana had been arrested two weeks before for gluing herself to the footpath at the Shell headquarters, and Sam for gluing himself to the doors of the InterContinental hotel on Park Lane during a petroleum conference. Not one to be outdone, around the same time Skeena had chained herself to a fence outside Labour leader Jeremy Corbyn's home.

All this made the question of whether to shake hands with the three more fraught than usual – and led to that loud conversation outside my office. My team were very keen for me not to get 'glued'. Overhearing them battle it out made me reflect on the bizarre nature of my job. As mayor, you very rarely get to see what I call the 'duck's legs' – the huge amount of kicking that goes on underneath the surface to keep the operation moving forward. I felt even more grateful than usual to my talented team, who are always on the lookout for risks: whether a PR misstep or, on this occasion, gluey hands.

In the end, the team advised I didn't shake the hands of Farhana, Sam and Skeena. But I chose to reject their advice. I'd seen Farhana and Sam give media interviews and it was clear that they were smart, determined and not stupid enough to waste an important meeting by getting out the Super Glue. It turned out to be the right call. As I walked into a meeting room on the eighth floor, we smiled and exchanged warm greetings. When we shook hands, there was no trace of glue.

But I wasn't out of the woods yet. Despite the initial friendliness, from the moment we sat down, it was clear that this would be a challenging meeting. The tone of the room soon turned serious, almost sombre.

I could understand why XR were wary. The group's cynical attitude to mainstream politicians was more widespread than I would have liked. One of the things that surprised me upon becoming mayor was how sceptical green activists and charities – not to mention businesses and pressure groups – were towards political leaders. In many cases, they thought I was just looking to score cheap political points, perhaps at their expense.

It was clear that to make my meeting with XR a success, I would have to draw on all the lessons I'd learned from three years as Mayor of London. There was surely a way to overcome their scepticism about mainstream politics. But how?

The statistics on people's levels of trust in politics make for depressing reading. Towards the end of the Second World War, only around one in three people in the UK saw politicians as 'out for themselves'. Today, that figure has doubled to almost two in three.[1] You can see why. Between the expenses scandal, the dishonesty of the Brexit campaign, and Prime Minister Boris Johnson's Downing Street parties during the Covid lockdowns, ours has become the age of political disillusionment. At the time of writing, three-quarters of people don't trust the government to take decisions that will improve their lives.[2]

This pattern holds true for climate change. Although the UK has one of the world's highest levels of concern regarding climate change – three-quarters of people say we must do 'everything necessary, urgently' in response – trust in politicians to deliver that change is low.[3] Sixty-nine per cent of Britons believe they are more concerned about the climate emergency than our current government is.[4]

Every politician has witnessed these corrosive levels of mistrust first-hand. During my attempts to run for mayor, I spent a lot of time with green environmental groups – from Friends of the Earth, to the Green Alliance, to the Labour Environment Campaign SERA. I enjoyed our discussions, and I learned a lot every time. I knew that as mayor I couldn't hope to please all nongovernmental organisations and pressure groups all the time, but I didn't see upsetting all of them all the time as a badge of pride like some politicians did. They weren't always so keen on me, though. Many of these groups were convinced that politicians were natural liars, and would never take the climate crisis as seriously as they should. They pointed out that the 2008 Climate Change Act, passed by the Labour government, was a distant memory – and its ambition had not been replicated by subsequent administrations. The great environmental hope, the 2016 Tory mayoral candidate Zac Goldsmith, had hardly mentioned these issues during his campaign to be mayor. Understandably, many politically engaged people were cynical about whether politicians were serious about tackling the climate crisis.

One incident in early 2016 hammered home the extent of this disillusionment. In March, I'd taken part in a hustings at the Royal Society of Medicine organised by Green Alliance, an independent think tank and charity focused on the environment. After the event had finished, the mayoral candidates joined the audience – made up of members of the public and representatives of environment groups – at a drinks reception. It was hosted in a foyer that had been filled with greenery for the occasion, bringing to mind the time then-Culture Secretary Jeremy Hunt allegedly hid behind a tree to avoid having to speak to journalists (he would have had a field day here, I thought). I was in high spirits until I was confronted by a member of the audience, who told me that she couldn't name a single politician who had delivered on their climate promises after being elected. She said that if I won the mayoralty, within months I would be focused on the 'bread-and-butter' issues of housing, transport and policing, and the relationships I'd been trying to establish with environment groups would be forgotten. As she got angrier and angrier, I'm proud to say I did not hide behind a tree (though I did think about it).

This cynicism wasn't just coming from activists. Among businesses, levels of trust in politicians were through the floor. The leadership of the Labour Party at the time didn't help. In my early years as mayor, Jeremy Corbyn was leader, which brought a certain baggage. Our position on Brexit had been unclear, and there were concerns that a Labour government could scare away much-needed private-sector investment. I was keen to meet CEOs and entrepreneurs to reassure them that I would be a pro-business mayor, and to tell them of the role I envisaged for the private sector in tackling the climate crisis. But this wasn't always easy. Many executives saw climate action as just another obstacle to their short-term profitability – understandable in a city where 90 per cent of companies are small businesses.

All this meant that by the time I arrived in City Hall, I was under no illusions about how much faith Londoners had in any politician with a green agenda. I recall meeting one green activist who pithily summarised what she saw as the problem: 'The trouble with you politicians is you always say one thing and do another.'

One of the things that most drew me to the Labour Party as a teenager was the fact that it's a coalition – made up of everyone from trade unionists to students, radical socialists to social democrats. Fired up with youthful political zeal, I was inspired by that most basic principle of the labour movement: that by the strength of our common endeavour we achieve more than we achieve alone.

I still find this idea inspiring today. Coalition-building is about coming together with people who don't share your political outlook. Take Lyndon B. Johnson, who was President of the United States from 1963 until 1969. His willingness to reach across the divides of American politics allowed him to pass the Civil Rights Act and the Voting Rights Act within two years of becoming president. Effective political leadership is about gaining the support of people who have different objectives to you, whether activists, businesses, or just engaged members of the public. While many of these people will be wary of your overtures, it's important to persevere. The overall goal is to assemble a group of diverse people around you, and harness their combined energy behind one singular goal.

Since my earliest days in politics, this has been my solution to disillusionment. By speaking to people with different views – and collaborating with them – you can begin to replace cynicism with hope.

In practice, this coalition-building usually involves following a few simple steps. First, talking to people with different political outlooks and trying as hard as you can to understand their concerns. The power of this kind of 'active listening' became clear during the 2016 mayoral campaign. Paddy Hennessy, a veteran journalist serving as my director of communications, had to explain to some of the younger, trendier members of my team the concept behind the 'prawn cocktail offensive'. This term was used to describe the Labour Party's attempt to win businesses' support in the 1990s by meeting corporate leaders, talking through their concerns, and setting out Labour's case in person. (Legend has it this typically took place over a prawn cocktail, although many who were there at the time deny the consumption of a single crustacean.) Paddy was keen for me to launch my own prawn cocktail offensive. The hipper members of my campaign staff, appalled by the un-chic 1970s imagery, urgently sought a rebrand. After some illuminating discussion, we settled on 'ceviche campaign' – ceviche, I learned, being a Peruvian seafood dish that was taking London's coolest eateries by storm.

One particularly nerve-wracking moment in our ceviche campaign was my meeting with Mike Bloomberg, the former Mayor of New York and one of the most successful businessmen in the world. His financial data company, Bloomberg, had a big presence in London, employing over 4,000 people, and he was building on a new European HQ in London. I was keen to meet Mike to show my pro-business credentials and to pick his brains about successfully running for mayor. But his support was not guaranteed. I was a relatively unknown politician and, having never met Mike before, I wasn't sure how we'd get on. The stakes were high. In addition to being a serious opinion-former, Bloomberg also runs a formidable media company. In Paddy's eyes, the downside of the meeting going badly was much larger than the upside of the meeting going well.

By the time I arrived at Bloomberg's London HQ, I was feeling nervous. I'd travelled from the London Labour campaign HQ, which was a massive upgrade from my squalid selection campaign office in Whitechapel (once the scene of an early-morning drama involving a dead mouse and a toaster). But as proud as I was of our newer, posher campaign office, the gleaming Bloomberg block was another world. During the meeting, my approach was simple: listen closely to what Mike was saying and try to actively take it on board.

Mike turned out to be incredibly down-to-earth. He was adamant that one of the smartest things you could do as a politician was to share an open-plan office with your team rather than shut yourself away. To the mild irritation of my campaign team, one of my first actions following the meeting was to give up my office and sit with them. First me texting them incessantly after my crack-of-dawn runs, now this. Mike subsequently became a mentor and friend, and I got to know his team well. Aside from being a successful businessman he was a world leader on climate change policy, and his advice was invaluable. A much-relieved Paddy returned to our campaign HQ telling the staff and volunteers I could roll with the best of them, 'whether the cleaner in a bus garage or an American billionaire'. In the years that followed, Mike would be a crucial part of our coalition to raise awareness about climate change. In 2018, he would approach internationally acclaimed artist Olafur Eliasson to display blocks of melting ice from Greenland at two public sites, the Tate Modern and the Bloomberg headquarters. The artwork, *Ice Watch*, sent a powerful message about the perils of climate change: as each block melted, it served as a visceral reminder about what was happening everywhere on earth, from Alpine glaciers to the Arctic.

Listening is not, by itself, enough to overcome people's cynicism. You need to back up your listening with action – ideally action of the most demonstrative, obvious kind. That has often meant following a simple rule: 'Get your hands dirty.' Unfortunately for me, my team have occasionally taken this instruction quite literally. I challenge anyone to think that the mayor's life is glamorous having seen me on 1 December 2018. That Saturday morning, I arrived in the East London borough of Redbridge to join an event that was part of our Trees for Cities campaign. As the site was just over a mile from the nearest Tube station, Ali Picton, who lived nearby, came to meet me and walk me over to where the volunteers were arriving.

The rain was biblical, the sky charcoal grey. I thought I had come prepared for the weather in my boots and a decent jacket. Alas, I soon discovered that my conception of 'weather appropriate' was wholly inadequate. Within minutes, freezing water was seeping through my gloves and boots, and my supposedly waterproof coat was soaked through. Things only deteriorated from there. When we arrived at our destination, we discovered that to access our designated field, we had to climb over a stile and then jump over a huge mud sinkhole. Ali completed this gymnastic exercise with characteristic grace. I did not. I'm not sure what was more entertaining for anyone driving past – my ungainly attempts to vault the fence, or those of the two burly police protection officers who followed suit.

This was really putting my money where my mouth was, I thought. The event was part of National Tree Week, in which people from across London would plant thousands of saplings to mark the start of the winter tree-planting season. It was part of my goal to make London the first ever National Park City, an election pledge that involved making London greener, healthier and wilder – enhancing the green belt, maintaining and growing our green spaces, and ultimately making more than half of our capital green.

Tree-planting has occasionally been something of a sore spot for my administration. One of the biggest mistakes I made when running for mayor in 2016 was saying in interviews and on my website that I would plant two million trees by 2020 – a 20 per cent increase in the number of trees in London. Once I'd made it to City Hall, I rapidly learned that this was simply impossible to deliver. Between a lack of suitable land and the limited capacity of boroughs and voluntary organisations, there was absolutely no way to plant this number of trees in five mayoral terms, let alone one. Even though this policy never made it to our manifesto, to this day it is raised by my political opponents: a reminder to always, always do your homework before announcing a policy.

One reason the two-million-tree target proved elusive was the simplest: planting trees takes people – lots of people. Even with our tree-planting target revised down to the hundreds of thousands, we soon realised we would need a huge coalition to achieve it. We required a tree-planting army, made up of school children and community groups, businesses and local politicians. That's why I found myself failing to jump over a fence in Redbridge that bleak December morning. The only way to win people round to the necessity of the cause was to take part in it myself.

As we planted tree after tree, stopping from time to time for a lukewarm cup of instant coffee and some brief respite from the rain under a leaky gazebo, we shared details of our lives and motivations for spending our Saturday together. Despite our differences in age, class and background, we all shared the same aim: to create a brighter, greener London. I ended the day covered in mud and exhausted, but excited too. That weekend over 80,000 trees were planted across our city. By the end of my first term as mayor, our tree-huggers' alliance had planted more than 340,000 saplings.

But above all, effective coalition-building is about finding ways to bring diverse groups of people together – and demonstrating to them that they have more in common than they think. An instructive example was the campaign against the expansion of Heathrow Airport which began with my election in 2016. Early in my campaign to be mayor, I had publicly outlined my opposition to a third runway. This surprised many within the Labour Party: just a few years previously I had voted in favour of the third runway in Parliament. Some of my opponents accused me not just of inconsistency, but political opportunism. There were several charming memes circulating on social media of my face superimposed on top of a flip-flop.

The truth was, in the years since voting for the Heathrow expansion, I had been on a political journey. On the campaign trail, I had met with groups like Greenpeace and the Heathrow Association for the Control of Aircraft Noise (HACAN), the residents' organisation that had been campaigning against a third runway for decades. They had told me about the 650 planes that landed at Heathrow every day – one plane every 45 seconds at the busiest times – which led to a near-constant stream of pollution drifting down from the sky. HACAN had also pointed me towards data showing that almost 10,000 Londoners a year were dying prematurely because of air pollution. Air pollution was making Londoners sick. It had made me sick. How could I say yes to a new runway?

But my new stance on Heathrow meant I had a lot of convincing to do. As mayor I couldn't unilaterally shut down plans for a third runway: the decision was ultimately in the hands of the government. And many of the existing groups campaigning against the third runway thought I was playing politics. I was, after all, the man who had been calling for one just a decade previously. Worse, many of these groups didn't get on among themselves: unsurprising, considering the anti-third-runway coalition ranged from Tory councils to radical air-pollution campaigners to giant NGOs.

So my goal was to bring together an eclectic band of activists, local councils and stakeholder groups who, between them, might convince the government to change tack. That meant very deliberately and carefully getting everyone to focus on what they had in common. On becoming mayor, I took the decision to personally chair TfL, London's transport authority, and directed them to provide legal advice and assistance to Greenpeace, as well as the London boroughs of Hammersmith and Fulham, Hillingdon, Richmond, Wandsworth, and the Royal Borough of Windsor and Maidenhead – only one of which was run by a Labour administration. Together, this coalition would build a much stronger case against the third runway than any one of these groups could ever hope to.

From the moment it was created, the coalition was a fragile thing. But it worked. I'll never forget the scenes outside the court in May 2019 at the end of the first judicial review. As a former lawyer, I knew it wasn't unusual for interested parties to show up outside the courtroom to try and gain support for their cause, particularly in more high-profile cases. But this was something else. The High Court wasn't just swamped with activists bearing placards, slogans and all manner of imaginative outfits – there were also besuited Tory councillors, retirees from the leafiest Windsor suburbs, and sympathetic business-people. Inside it was standing room only: I arrived to find my team had aggressively occupied a seat for me along-side Labour MP John McDonnell, who was chatting happily away to a most unlikely bedfellow, the Conser-vative leader of Uxbridge council. Our coalition. And we had won the day: our combined legal action secured a number of vital concessions, including that meeting air-quality obligations was the 'reddest of red lines'. The third runway could not proceed without significant pro-tection for air quality in London. The battle that followed wasn't easy – in 2020, the Court of Appeal finally ruled that the government's decision to proceed with building the third runway was unlawful, only for that decision to subsequently be overruled by the Supreme Court – but at every stage this strange cross-London alliance was on the front line.

Most interesting of all was the effect the campaign had on my relationship with my supposed political oppon-ents. I had seen some of the cynicism I'd faced ease, even from groups that had long been sceptical about both City Hall and the Labour Party. Perhaps my actions had even started to restore their faith in politicians: one group of campaigners told us that we'd met all the demands their whole team had on air quality. In the years since my election, I have often wondered about that activist I spoke to after the Green Alliance hustings in 2016. I hope I've helped convince her that politicians aren't all the same.

As Farhana, Sam and Skeena sat opposite me in the meeting room in City Hall, all of these experiences were running through my head. The three weren't hostile per se; in fact, they were impeccably polite. But, within minutes, a certain frostiness had descended on the conversation. XR were not a group who tended to like politicians very much.

The first few minutes of our conversation went well enough, with questions about City Hall's climate credentials. Just a few months previously I had declared a climate emergency, making London one of the first cities in the world to do so. XR understandably wanted to be shown that this wasn't just a PR stunt and to hear about my strategy to tackle the crisis. I explained that we'd adopted a target for London to reach net zero by 2030 and had implemented an independently verified Climate Action Plan that was compatible with the Paris Climate Accords to keep global warming within 1.5 °C. That seemed to go down quite well.

But then we entered choppier waters. The trio wanted us to move even further and faster. They were particularly adamant that I create a 'citizens' assembly': a group of ordinary people to investigate, discuss and make recommendations on how to respond to the climate emergency. Similar to jury service, members would be randomly selected from across the country.

Earlier in my career, I may have simply shut this idea down. I've never been a fan of such initiatives, because I've seen little evidence that they work. I thought such an assembly sounded like a recipe for disaster. What if the people who were selected didn't want to develop the UK's climate policy? I opened my mouth and prepared to express my doubts.

But then I paused. An image dropped into my head: a group of green activists, Tory councillors, and retirees from the suburbs sat together in a back room, bashing out our campaign to stop the third runway. I hadn't agreed with many of them on many policies either. Yet those meetings had been among the most constructive of my career.

That memory informed my response to XR. It was understandable that people were disillusioned with politicians on climate. But if the people around this table might disagree on the strategy, we all shared the same objective. And so that's what I said. Despite my reservations, I agreed to explore the citizens' assembly idea, and to convene a meeting with academics, councils and policy experts to explore how such a body might be run.

It worked. You could feel the tension in the room deflate – and within a few minutes, we were talking constructively and even sharing the odd joke. By the end of the meeting, everyone seemed relatively happy. I was impressed by the way Farhana, Sam and Skeena put some of their own personal views to one side to make the meeting a success. And hopefully I convinced them that I was taking the climate threat seriously – even if we didn't completely agree about what to do in response. I said goodbye and returned promptly to my office, keen to reassure my team that I was both unscathed and unglued.

I wasn't lying when I promised to look into citizens' assemblies. Since 2019, a number of councils in London have held such assemblies specifically on climate. And, while I'm still not a complete convert, I can see their benefit: they get a diverse array of people in a room together to talk about the environment. Unfortunately, in the wake of their later protests, those collaborative conversations with XR would become harder. I believe passionately in the right to protest; I was a human rights lawyer, after all. But I feel that to protest in ways that are unlawful or dangerous (and in the case of XR it was often both) was counterproductive.

Yet to this day, when I'm feeling pessimistic about the prospects of our climate change agenda, I reflect on that meeting with Farhana, Sam and Skeena. Cynicism, I often think, breeds cynicism. If just one person around a table thinks anyone else is acting in bad faith, then soon everyone will be in a foul mood – and progress will become impossible. But if you think of politics as a way of reaching across such divides, it becomes possible to surmount those tensions – and to replace cynicism with optimism. It worked with our tree-planting campaign. It worked with Heathrow. And to date, I've never been Super-Glued.

Obstacle 4

Deprioritisation

We almost made it.

It was March 2020, and my campaign to be re-elected Mayor of London was in full swing. Over the previous few months, my team and I had got back into the rhythm of campaign life – knocking on doors, speaking to voters and hiring new staff. The opposing political parties had chosen their candidates, and I was excited about the hustings and debates that were beginning to be confirmed in my calendar.

I have always loved election campaigns. There is no other context in which you meet so many people, with such an eclectic array of views, in such a short space of time. The year 2020 was no different. Former Tory minister Rory Stewart had thrown his hat in the ring and was currently offering to stay on Londoners' sofas to 'learn more about London' in a scheme he'd badged #ComeKipWithMe. I thought this election was going to be memorable.

I couldn't have known how right I was. In January I had been on my way to one of my regular People's Question Time events: town-hall meetings where members of the public can ask me whatever they like. As usual, my staff were briefing me on what issues might come up. On my way to the venue in Haringey, a colleague mentioned a flu-like virus that was spreading in China and was starting to get media attention. While there were no cases in the UK at that time, I asked what the advice was to anyone with symptoms. I was surprised to hear that the strict advice was to 'stay at home' and not visit your doctor or hospital unless you needed urgent medical attention. I was even more surprised when someone did indeed ask a question about it later that night. That was the first time the word 'Coronavirus' entered my consciousness.

As I travelled back to Tooting, I had no idea how Coronavirus was set to shape the following weeks, months and years of my mayoralty. By the end of that month, the disease had spread rapidly: first through China, then Italy, and then Britain. Our TV screens were flooded with shocking images of overfull hospitals in Wuhan, then Milan. As Covid climbed up the news agenda, we continued campaigning as best we could. In February we stopped door-knocking and started contacting voters by phone. Events and even fundraisers moved online. We war-gamed several scenarios to consider how the virus would affect turnout on election day. Before I knew it, we were approaching the start of the 'short campaign' – the five-week period after which a person has officially become a candidate. We still thought the election was going to go ahead.

And then everything changed.

By mid-March, the full scale of the impending crisis was beginning to become apparent. Once again, my position on shaking hands was causing drama. Rumours abounded about how the virus spread, and considering how much time I spend meeting people, particularly during election time, I made a personal decision to stop shaking hands with those I met. This raised a few eyebrows. That week, Prime Minister Boris Johnson had confirmed that he intended to keep shaking hands with 'everybody' and had bragged about doing so on a visit to a hospital with Covid-19 patients.

By this point, the atmosphere at City Hall was one of solemn concern. Coronavirus was spreading fast, particularly in London, and people were starting to panic. I'd organised a rare Mayoral Advisory Group (MAG) meeting at City Hall – a kind of London equivalent to a government COBRA meeting, convened to handle matters of national emergency – and met with the Chief Medical Officer, Professor Chris Whitty. We took the decision to cancel the St Patrick's Day Parade, despite official government advice not yet recommending the cancellation of mass gatherings.

I would have done anything to ensure the election went ahead on 7 May. But suddenly, rumours started to circulate that the government was planning to postpone it. I desperately didn't want this to happen. The campaign was firing on all cylinders. My team tried to speak to whomever they could in government to find out what was happening. If the elections were to be delayed, then for how long? (A month? Six months?) But to no avail. The news was finally confirmed on the inauspicious afternoon of Friday 13 March. Local, mayoral and police and crime commissioner elections would all be postponed until May 2021 on the advice of the government's medical experts.

It was the right decision, but it was a blow. My campaign team were bitterly disappointed. I later found out that on hearing the news they downed tools and went to the local pub en masse. They were soon joined by many friends in the wider Team Khan group, who had been volunteering to support my re-election. The mood was dire. Political campaigns are all-consuming. Everyone in my team had been working flat-out for weeks, and now it had all come to nothing. Worse, several members of the campaign staff were on fixed-term contracts, and would now be out of a job. To lift my spirits, a friend sent a message congratulating me on my 'one-year re-election'. That was certainly one way to look at it.

Over the next few days, my spirits sank even further. On Monday morning, I received my first invite to a COBRA meeting on Covid-19 – joining the prime minister, the Cabinet and leaders from the devolved administrations in Scotland, Wales and Northern Ireland to hear that, in terms of the virus, London was 'a few weeks' ahead of the rest of the country. The rate of infection in the capital was far higher, and the virus spreading far quicker, than anywhere else in the UK.

The news hit me in the same way my asthma diagnosis had a few years previously. Once again, I'd been blindsided. Once again, that had been avoidable. There was information that could have enabled me to act, but I hadn't been given access to it. I could not understand how London had not been included in the government's Coronavirus planning until this point. London was served by four big airports and the Eurostar. We were a global city, a hub for people from around the world – and a gateway for the virus.

I knew we would have to be straight with Londoners about the scale of the crisis we were facing. Immediately after leaving the COBRA meeting I changed my advice, asking Londoners to stay at home and not to use public transport. That Friday, 20 March, the COBRA meeting decided that pubs, restaurants and gyms would be ordered to close. The decision led to the strangest media round I'd ever undertaken, announcing that until further notice, we were closing down the city. The mood was apocalyptic; some of those filming the interviews were wearing thick face coverings, which I hadn't encountered before. As I left 4 Millbank, the building where many of the television and broadcast studios are based, I had a feeling that things were never going to be the same again.

On Monday 23 March the prime minister announced

that the UK would go into a full lockdown. For the next seven weeks, people across the country could only leave home to exercise once a day, travel to and from work when it was 'absolutely necessary', shop for essential items, or fulfil their medical or care needs. Shops selling non-essential goods – from hairdressers to hospitality outlets – were shuttered, and meetings of more than two people who did not live together were forbidden.

Covid-19 was devastating. In London, more than 20,000 people lost their lives. Like so many Londoners, I lost loved ones. I will never forget the heartbreaking stories I heard about people being unable to say good-bye, funerals taking place without family members, and grieving friends and relatives left with no ability to console one another in person.

In those early weeks, I barely had time to think about what Coronavirus meant for my wider objectives as Mayor of London. But in the moments I did, I felt morose. During a crisis like Covid, everything else gets dropped. Rightly, the focus becomes saving lives first, and saving the economy second – all your wider policies, from climate to housing to education, get left by the wayside. I worried this would be particularly true of my environmental strategy. In just a few weeks, we had lost momentum on climate. We had intended to fight the May election on extending the ULEZ to 18 times its existing size – so it would cover an area four times larger than Paris. Londoners seemed to be with me. Now, thanks to the delayed election, this policy wouldn't be rolled out until sometime after May 2021.

At this rate, my climate agenda was going to go out the window. I was going to spend the rest of my (suddenly extended) term witnessing my climate achievements unravel; all while being unable to introduce new climate policies because of the Covid catastrophe that was consuming my every waking hour. Against an unprecedented crisis of this kind, was there any way to stop my climate strategy getting derailed?

As Billy Ocean didn't quite sing in his 1985 hit, 'When the going gets tough, the climate gets forgotten.' This is a pattern that has played out time and again in recent years. Politicians campaign on an ambitious platform to tackle climate change; the public seem enthusiastic, and elect the politician in a landslide; and then, when in office, climate sinks further and further down the agenda.

In the 2010 general election, David Cameron memorably encouraged voters to 'Vote Blue, Go Green'. But just a few years later, he reportedly ordered his staff to 'get rid of all the green crap'.[1] However, this is not just a tendency on the right. In the lead-up to the COP15 climate change conference in Copenhagen in 2009, President Barack Obama made several big promises on climate. But the following year, his climate change bill was abandoned in the US Senate in the face of opposition from both sides of the chamber.

The reason for this kind of deprioritisation is simple. Being in power involves constant firefighting: you're battling urgent problem after urgent problem, and so the kind of long-term planning that climate policy requires gets overlooked. The urgent always overtakes the important. And everything apart from climate change seems to be urgent.

I had always told myself that my climate policies would never get blown off course in this way. But during those early days of the Covid pandemic, I could see it happening in real-time. As that horrific first lockdown wore on, the priority was getting doctors, nurses and staff to hospitals, which meant ensuring those who needed to could move freely across the capital. We immediately suspended the Central London Congestion Charge, Low Emission Zone (LEZ) and ULEZ to allow key workers to travel safely for free during the strictest period of lockdown. At the same time, we limited London's public transport capacity to one-fifth of pre-crisis levels to enable safe social distancing. This meant that up to eight million journeys a day would need to be made by other means. We knew that, in practice, that would mean people getting back into their cars. Obviously, these were exceptional circumstances. But our fear was that a higher level of car usage would continue after the lockdown lifted. Reports from our contacts in Chinese cities told us that as soon as they opened up, car use had increased by 60 per cent on pre-pandemic numbers. London would be gridlocked, and Londoners would be exposed to toxic traffic fumes at levels far worse than ever before. We were right to be concerned. By the end of lockdown, car traffic on weekdays in Central London surpassed pre-lockdown levels.

In the weeks that followed, the situation became even more dire. By the summer we found we were battling not only for our climate policies, but for our political careers. The government launched a full assault on City Hall. Since 2016, we had reduced TfL's deficit by 71 per cent, and for the first time in TfL's history had reduced operating costs. At the same time, we had frozen TfL fares to encourage more Londoners to use public transport instead of driving. But as the lockdown wore on, TfL's finances imploded. Unlike other transport authorities around the world, TfL is funded largely through the revenue it raises through fares from commuters: 72 per cent of the services TfL provides are paid for by customers using the Tube, buses, trams and the Overground, compared to 39 per cent in New York City and Paris, and 21 per cent in Singapore.[2] Now, with most Londoners staying at home, TfL's income plummeted. We were receiving from customers only a fraction of the £600 million it cost to run transport in London every four weeks, and burning through our cash reserves at a worrying pace.

Our only choice was to turn to the government. Boris Johnson's administration had unconditionally supported other train operating companies and businesses during the lockdown – so we assumed they'd be similarly helpful in our case. We were mistaken. The government attached onerous conditions to funding support for TfL. It was clear their intention was to try and turn public opinion against me, with an eye on the mayoral election now scheduled for the following year. The ulterior motive was blatant, but they had me over a barrel: I couldn't allow a situation where I was having to cut essential Tube lines or bus routes in the middle of a pandemic. So I had no choice but to accept some draconian measures, not only to reintroduce the Congestion Charge, but to bring forward proposals to temporarily widen its scope and level. From June, the Congestion Charge was increased from £11.50 to £15, and would be in place seven days a week from 7am until 10pm, rather than Monday to Friday from 7am to 6pm.

This was the worst of all worlds. The increase in the Congestion Charge did initially reduce the amount of car traffic in Central London to below pre-lockdown levels, but the numbers soon crept back up again. Meanwhile, the transport network remained on precarious financial footing. And my wider climate strategy had been blown wildly off course. It seemed I was becoming yet another politician in the Billy Ocean school: faced with a crisis, the environment was rapidly getting bumped down the to-do list.

By June, I was feeling misanthropic. At the forefront of my mind were the catastrophic health and economic effects of the lockdown on Londoners. But personally, I was also finding lockdown really difficult. Like many in the capital, for almost eight weeks I barely left my home apart from a daily walk with our Labrador, Luna, to Tooting Common. I knew I was lucky. Unlike millions of people in London and around the country, I had a decent-sized home and garden, a family whom I love and enjoy spending time with, and a very excitable dog. But with my daughters home from university and Saadiya working from home too, I was finding it difficult to balance work with the rest of my life.

I spent most of the day working from my dining-room table, in front of two doors that led into our kitchen. Unfortunately, the UK's big media hits – whether morning news shows like *BBC Breakfast* or *Good Morning Britain*, or the lunchtime or evening regional bulletins – tend to coincide with mealtimes. That meant that BBC and Sky News interviews were often chaotically interrupted by the noise of the NutriBullet, the toaster and loud family conversations. My team, watching or listening remotely, would often remark that they could hear Luna barking in the background. During some interviews I resorted to feeding her treats under the table to keep her quiet.

I'm used to stressful situations, but as someone who thrives on getting out and about, lockdown took its toll on my mental health. I stopped shaving every day, and if I wasn't on a Zoom with people from outside City Hall

I'd revert to wearing worn-out old T-shirts. Once, following an all-staff call in which I'd worn my grey tracksuit, I discovered I'd gone viral on the City Hall staff network because of my new look. Whenever I wore the outfit Saadiya, who is used to seeing clients in prison, told me I was dressed like an inmate.

I remember sitting down for an interview with Decca Aitkenhead from the *Sunday Times* a few weeks after the lockdown started to lift. It was one of the first interviews I had undertaken from a still very empty City Hall – a 'mausoleum' as Decca described it – and the sheer scale of what our city had been through was starting to hit home. Decca, an infamously brilliant interviewer among politicians, managed to tease out the reality of my mood. 'I found it really tough,' I found myself saying. 'There are days when I'm not providing proper leadership.' This wasn't planned. My advisors knew nothing about how I was feeling, let alone that I was going to announce it to the world.[3]

But then Decca started to ask about my environmental policies. And unexpectedly I started to feel better. During our conversation, the penny dropped. Yes, the pandemic was an unprecedented health crisis. But it was also an opportunity. There were, I found myself telling Decca, 'some potential silver linings'. Truth be told, that interview was the first time I had actually managed to spot them.

Suddenly, I could see everything more clearly. We

could not replace a Covid-19 health crisis with an air-quality crisis, sparked by a return to pre-ULEZ levels of car use. The transformation of London over the previous few months represented a unique chance to reshape our city. I was determined to grasp it. 'I don't want a car-led recovery, I want a green-led recovery,' I said.

Out of nowhere, I remembered a line often attributed to Winston Churchill: 'Never let a good crisis go to waste.' Supposedly uttered during the attempts to build the UN from the ruins of the Second World War, this is a valuable insight for any politician. Our history is peppered with moments when crises have led to the transformation of a society, often for the better. Sometimes, the fear generated by a disaster enables leaders to make bold policy moves. In 2011, for example, a huge tsunami hit the north-east coast of Japan, causing four of the six nuclear reactors at the Fukushima plant to release radiation into the atmosphere and ocean. Following the disaster, German Chancellor Angela Merkel quickly reversed her position on nuclear energy and announced that Germany would gradually shut down all nuclear power plants by 2022 – paving the way for Germany to become independent of both nuclear energy and coal. Necessity is the mother of invention: and nothing necessitates invention like a disaster.

It was difficult for me to think this, let alone say it aloud, in early 2020. But Coronavirus was just such an opportunity. While some Londoners were taking to their cars to avoid public transport, even more were doing the opposite. For the first time in decades, millions of Londoners were walking and cycling around the city, and realising they enjoyed it. My Twitter feed was increasingly filled with photos of people out on their bikes across London, many for the first time in their lives.

This was a chance to put into practice some of the most exciting new ideas about 21st-century cities. A few years previously, I'd read about Carlos Moreno, a French-Colombian scientist who proposed the concept of a '15-minute city', where residents could access six essential functions within a 15-minute walk or bike ride from their home: living, working, commerce, healthcare, education and entertainment.[4] Many of my European counterparts were enthused by the idea. Anne Hidalgo, standing for re-election in Paris, made the *ville du quart d'heure* a pillar of her campaign. Might Covid present an opportunity to bring the 15-minute city to London?

We started to develop in ever-greater detail how that might work. If we could find a way to make pedestrian and cycle journeys safe and desirable, then many people might never return to their polluting cars – and London's air would become even cleaner. We just needed a method to make it happen. That method would be London Streetspace.

The idea for Streetspace was simple. We'd create new protected cycle lanes, extending pavements and also helping to reduce traffic in residential areas. This would make it easier and safer for people to walk, cycle and use public transport. Under the leadership of Walking and Cycling Commissioner Will Norman and City Hall advisor Will Bradley, the plan started to take shape. The Two Wills – as they inevitably became known – had already begun to identify what schemes we had in the pipeline that we could accelerate. Next, working with TfL, they pulled together a list of places where work wasn't already underway but should be. The detail was remarkable – I was presented with maps showing individual streets where scores of people on tiny pavements were queuing for a bus or waiting to go into the bank, with no opportunity to social distance. Armed with this fearsome bank of information, we were able to approach councils across the city to request they put in bids for areas where they wanted to build cycle lanes, widen footways, and create low-traffic neighbourhoods (LTNs).

Not all councils were keen on the plans. Some, like Kensington and Chelsea, chose to behave in a narrow-minded way – making the notorious decision to rip out a much-needed segregated cycle route along Kensington High Street just seven weeks after it was installed under the Streetspace programme. But inside City Hall, we focused our attention on the groups that were supportive of Streetspace. We called them the 'coalition of the willing', a coalition that included everyone from the national government (who were supporting us in this, at least), to local councils like Hackney, Lambeth and

Southwark, to campaign groups like the walking charity Living Streets.

The effects on London were transformative. First, Streetspace sparked a cycling revolution. Since lockdown began, TfL had already made 1,700 more cycle hire bikes available, bringing the grand total to more than 14,000 – an increase of nearly 15 per cent and the largest single increase in bikes for the scheme since 2013. Streetspace would help make much of this change permanent. In the first six months after the scheme was launched in May, almost 100 kilometres of new or upgraded cycle lanes were built. This meant we had more than 250 kilometres of safe cycle lanes, more than any comparable global city. By the end of the year, Streetspace had seen the number of Londoners living within 400 metres of the London-wide cycle network almost double.[5]

I experienced the benefits of these cycle lanes firsthand. Following some sound advice from Will Norman and my senior aide Chris McQuiggin, I had invested in a new foldaway electric-assist bike from the London-based company Brompton. Soon I was cycling everywhere – much to the delight of my staff, who had finally found a way to get periodic breaks from my incessant texts and emails (I did try to text while waiting at traffic lights, with limited success). My police protection team were less thrilled. Politicians tend to drive, not cycle, and so they had to rapidly develop a bespoke training course:

'Protecting a mayor who won't stop cycling around Central London (very slowly)'.

In spite of my newfound identity as a MAMIL ('middle-aged man in Lycra' – or, in my case, 'in linen suit'), we were keen for pedestrians to feel the benefits of Streetspace too. Over a six-month period, 22,500 square metres of extra pavement space was reallocated to people walking.[6] Then there was our School Streets programme, which placed restrictions on traffic outside schools at drop-off and pick-up times – it had first begun in Camden in 2017, but the numbers of schemes delivered during the pandemic increased exponentially, with over 500 School Streets now in place.[7] At the same time, footways were expanded outside busy commuter hubs such as London Bridge, Victoria and Waterloo stations. But the most high-profile pedestrianisation policy to take hold during the pandemic was the LTN. Sometimes referred to colloquially as 'mini-Hollands' after similar infrastructure projects in the Netherlands, LTNs helped to make streets around London easier to walk and cycle on by stopping cars, vans and other vehicles from using quiet roads as shortcuts. Despite being around since the 1970s, emergency funding from the government during the pandemic saw over 70 schemes rolled out in a matter of months.[8]

On a Sunday morning in September 2020, I went for a cycle with my daughters. It was a beautiful early-autumn day: the air was crisp, the sky clear, and the trees on every road were ablaze with fiery reds and oranges. Anisah and Ammarah were also recent cycling converts, and had been emboldened by the new generation of cycle lanes and the relatively vehicle-free streets. From our home in Tooting, we cycled north to the River Thames at Battersea Park, and then on to Hyde Park before looping around and back home through Lambeth.

The London we encountered was unrecognisable. We saw hundreds of cyclists out and about. As we cycled through Brixton, we saw an LTN in action: people eating al fresco and chatting over a cup of coffee on a previously polluted road. Clearly I was not the only person enjoying the new London. By the end of 2020, we had received data confirming that walking and cycling in the capital had significantly increased since the pandemic began, with Londoners' travel habits rapidly changing in the months following the start of the first national lockdown and the introduction of Streetspace. The proportion of bicycle and walking journeys had increased from 29 per cent pre-pandemic to an estimated 46 per cent post-lockdown.[9]

In a matter of months, we'd reshaped our city – with enormous economic and social benefits. But for me, the truly fascinating part of the story was the impact on the health of Londoners – and notably the quality of our air. We'd suspected that the massive social changes brought about by lockdown would have a big impact on air quality. But we couldn't be sure whether they would last. Fortunately, on my team we had a brilliant head of air quality, Elliot Treharne: a man I suspect spent most of lockdown watching the London Air website just as everyone else was bingeing box-sets on Netflix. During the pandemic, Elliot and the team worked hard to ensure that the air-quality monitoring network could be maintained.

The results were intriguing. In the first few months of the pandemic we had published our first batch of expert-reviewed data. London had seen dramatic improvements in its air quality since the first lockdown, with dangerous emissions at some of the capital's busiest roads and junctions falling by almost 50 per cent. This mirrored what we were seeing in cities and countries across the world, as they came to a standstill to battle Covid-19 outbreaks; my fellow mayors in Paris, Milan, Madrid and New York noticed similar patterns. There were some fantastic photos of people in northern India seeing the Himalayas for the first time in their lives, thanks to the reduced air-pollution levels.

What was even more fascinating, though, was the data from after lockdown lifted. I had taken it upon myself not to 'waste' the crisis. In that we were successful. In late 2020, new data from King's College and Imperial College London showed dramatic improvements in air quality across the capital since 2016. Overall, air pollution had plunged since 2016, with a 94 per cent reduction in the number of people living in areas with illegal levels of nitrogen dioxide.[10] But what was most heartening was that the changes brought about by lockdown seemed to be sticking. A third of Londoners were now walking to places where they used to travel by a different mode, and even as restrictions eased, rates of walking and cycling remained well above their earlier levels. Independent world-leading experts said the reductions showed the air-pollution crisis was not intractable.

Most excitingly of all, Londoners were on board with this transformation. The trouble with Churchill's line about never wasting a crisis is that it sounds undemocratic – you're seizing on a disaster to pursue your own agenda. But for City Hall, it was imperative that Londoners were supportive of the changes we made to improve air quality. And supportive they were. A poll commissioned by London Councils found that 82 per cent of people recognised a change in air quality during the lockdown period.[11] Nearly nine in ten Londoners were now in favour of measures to reduce car emissions and use.[12] Lockdown had revolutionised people's approach to the environment, seemingly for good.

In the months that followed, I often found myself thinking about what Covid could teach policymakers interested in the environment. It was an outlier. Usually, when times get hard, tough climate policy immediately gets jettisoned. But in this case, the opposite had happened. Why?

Perhaps it was that the pandemic had brought out

Londoners' sense of solidarity. While the virus had a direct impact on all of us as individuals, our response was collective. Amid all the heartbreak, we witnessed some amazing, inspirational stories of generosity and courage. Young people dropping off shopping for the elderly. People making PPE at their kitchen tables. The weekly Clap for Our Carers, which saw millions of Londoners stop what they were doing every Thursday at 8pm to applaud the efforts of our NHS (the brainchild of a South Londoner, Annemarie Plas). Londoners had come together to overcome Covid. In doing so, they had created a rare opportunity to deal with air pollution too.

I was feeling the benefits of this transformation myself. By the end of the summer, I was using my inhalers and asthma medicine far less and felt great. And a good thing too. Because just under a year after our false start, I arrived at a youth club in South London to finally mark the first day of the short campaign. We had an election to fight.

Obstacle 5
Hostility

It was five weeks before the 2021 mayoral election, and I was being nuzzled by a horse.

This was, on the face of it, an unusual state of affairs. The final few weeks leading up to polling day are among the most intense moments in a politician's life. Every minute counts: for all our months of campaigning, it's only at the very end that voters' attention starts to turn to who they might actually vote for.

However, Eddie the horse seemed to have very little understanding of the precious nature of my time at this moment in the electoral calendar. In fact, he seemed primarily interested in eating oats (helpfully provided by the stablewoman) and wandering contentedly around the paddock. What was I doing here?

My visit to Ebony Horse Club in Brixton was not, in fact, inspired by a late-onset passion for farmyard animals. It was the idea of my long-time colleague Jack Stenner, who had just been appointed as my campaign manager. Over the years Jack had been instrumental in shaping my political messaging. It's largely down to him that the mere mention of me being the son of a bus driver is met with a groan and a laugh. In the 2021 election, Jack was very keen to hammer home a particular message: this was a two-horse race between me and my Conservative rival, Shaun Bailey. Jack was also very fond of visual metaphors. And so here I was, tentatively feeding oats to Eddie.

Although I was apprehensive of the visit – it broke two of the three components of the rule 'Never work with celebrities, children or animals' – the Ebony Horse Club was exactly the kind of initiative I wanted my administration to support. Situated in the heart of Brixton, with train tracks running overhead, the club enables young people living in South London to ride horses and learn to care for animals. Khadijah Mellah – the first hijab-wearing jockey to take part in (and then win) a competitive British horse race – trained at Ebony after seeing a flyer advertising the club in a local mosque. I was proud that City Hall had helped Ebony along the way. During my first term as mayor, we had invested over £70 million in a Young Londoners Fund, and Ebony Horse Club had received funding to provide weekly horse-riding lessons to young people who would not normally have had access to the sport.

The campaign's director of communications, Sarah Brown, had orchestrated the event perfectly. As it was the first official day of the five-week short campaign, there were far more media present than on my previous visits to Ebony. The BBC London political editor Tim

Donovan, an excellent journalist but known mischief-maker, had already clocked that one of the horses shared the same name as the Tory candidate: Bailey. I didn't want to mention my main opponent as it could enhance his name recognition. Tim, meanwhile, spent much of his interview trying to get me to comment on said horse. (I won. Message discipline!)

In the end, thanks to the helpful staff and surprisingly well-behaved horses, the visit went without a hitch. We ended the morning with a photocall: me holding the reins of two horses. Jack, never a fan of needlessly subtle political messaging, had suggested we adorn them with a rosette each – one red, one blue. The two-horse race had begun.

With a record number of candidates having put their hat in the ring, this message was more important than ever. The mayoral race would be contested by 20 people, among them several distinctive characters: from anti-vaxxer Piers Corbyn (the brother of Jeremy) to self-professed urine-drinker Brian Rose. The right was out in force, with candidates ranging from former actor Laurence Fox to the UKIP candidate Peter Gammons. None of them had a chance against the sole outsider candidate we were really worried about: the fearsome campaigner and voice of the people Count Binface.

The sheer number of candidates wasn't the only unusual feature of the 2021 election, however. It was taking place a year late, in a world transformed by Covid (and with restrictions still in place on indoor gatherings and rallies). And it was clear from the outset that for many Londoners, climate issues were now at the top of the agenda. It looked like it might just be the green election I was hoping for in 2016.

But at the same time, our green agenda was facing more – and louder – opposition than ever. While in 2016 we had struggled to get the attention we wanted for our climate policies, this time round we had the opposite problem: they were the subject of intense scrutiny, and in many cases organised attacks.

As the short campaign wore on, we found that our green agenda was facing down fierce criticism everywhere: in the newspapers, outside our campaign rallies, and on social media. We soon realised that the game had changed since 2016. Last time, the biggest obstacle to our green agenda had been apathy. This time, it was hostility.

On 3 November 1969, President Richard Nixon appeared on US television to criticise the 'vocal minority' who were protesting the war in Vietnam. Over the previous year, the streets of many American cities had been shut down by increasingly tumultuous and high-profile peace protests. In his famous address, Nixon played down the activists' concerns, appealing instead to 'the great silent majority of my fellow Americans': those who supported his plan to end the war by first ramping it up.[1] His point was that, while a small minority of progressive activists made all the noise, the real heart of America was quietly conservative.

Ever since, the terms 'silent majority' and 'vocal minority' have largely been associated with the right. Ronald Reagan used the phrase in his presidential campaigns throughout the 1980s. More recently, Donald Trump invoked the 'silent majority' in response to the protests at the murder of George Floyd – although, in classic Trump style, it wasn't wholly clear who he thought this majority were or what they wanted.

This chequered history means progressives have often been wary of invoking the idea of a 'silent majority'. Except, when it came to climate change, this was exactly what we were dealing with. The polling evidence was clear: the bulk of the British public thought climate change was a major issue. In 2021, 82 per cent of Londoners were concerned about climate change, with more than two-thirds saying their level of concern had risen in the last year.[2] Yet when you read the news or turned on the TV, you could be forgiven for thinking that climate change was a divisive issue, with large segments of the public opposed to strong environmental action.

Why? Because there was a small but often very loud group of individuals strongly voicing opinions on the climate that weren't (and aren't) particularly widespread. Whether it's by organising Twitter pile-ons, ringing up radio stations or starting petitions, they tend to exaggerate the support they have. Brought together with a mainstream media that is determined to give these people a platform, you have a toxic combination. So politicians get nervous and back down from tough action on climate.

Take the heatwave of summer 2022, in which temperatures in London topped 40°C for the first time in history. The *Daily Mail* ran with the headline: 'Sunny day snowflake Britain had a meltdown.' The only mention of the climate crisis was a photograph of climate protesters described in the caption as 'prolonging the misery'. An editorial suggested the UK's reaction to the unprecedented heat was a sign of weakness in the national character: 'Listening to apocalyptic climate change pundits and the BBC, you'd think Britain was about to spontaneously combust,' the *Mail* wrote.[3] Writing for the *Daily Express*, climate-sceptic columnist James Whale claimed, falsely, that 'planets move and we have been getting closer to the sun for thousands of years. Climate fluctuates over centuries.'[4] Similarly, the *Spectator*'s Brendan O'Neill asked: 'Is anyone else tiring of all this green hysteria over the heatwave?'[5] What all these articles have in common is their disregard for the actual evidence. To give just one of many, many such statistics, the 12 hottest days in history in the UK have all taken place since 2002.

During the 2021 election, this vocal minority were louder than ever. Take low-traffic neighbourhoods.

A small group opposing these schemes had drowned out the bulk of residents who were in favour of more pedestrianisation and traffic-calming measures. Polling undertaken in 2020 showed a majority of Londoners were in favour of LTN schemes.[6] In my 2021 manifesto, I pledged to work with London boroughs to ensure communities and stakeholder groups were properly consulted on these schemes – refining them where necessary, making them permanent where they were successful.

As the election campaign got underway, this became a classic 'vocal minority' issue. A hostile media seized upon LTNs as an example of an overbearing City Hall. Hyperbolic headlines from the *Daily Mail* included: 'London goes to WAR with Sadiq's "illegal" road schemes.'[7] Another *Mail* article claimed, incorrectly, that LTNs had made air pollution worse (or, to be precise, 'WORSE').[8] This media agenda was backed by a small network of anti-LTN activists – often made up of residents' groups without particularly wide support, but with very loud voices, especially on social media.

My political opponents spotted an opportunity. Shaun Bailey seized on the media narrative to make LTNs a bigger issue than they were and to artificially amplify the level of public opposition. Bailey attacked LTNs, claiming without evidence that they were causing gridlock (in one case describing an LTN as 'a road that has been shut down by the council and Sadiq Khan – without residents ever getting a say').[9] He promised repeatedly to remove 'unwanted' LTNs.

This policy was woolly in the extreme. Bailey hadn't made clear how he would establish which LTNs were 'unwanted' and which weren't. Nor had he acknowledged that as mayor he simply would not have the power to scrap them – they are implemented by London borough councils, not City Hall. In fact, the statutory guidance telling councils to introduce such measures – along with the funding – came from the Conservative government, not me.

But the disingenuousness of these statements didn't mean they weren't politically effective. Bailey had created a clear dividing line between the only two candidates that could realistically win the election. By inaccurately suggesting there was mass public opposition to LTNs – despite all the evidence to the contrary – Bailey managed to turn a non-issue into one of the biggest themes of the short campaign. Soon, I found myself talking about LTNs in large numbers of interviews, including at one of the first visits of the campaign.

A few weeks before my visit to Ebony Horse Club, I'd headed north to the Hot Milk Cafe in Enfield for my campaign's media launch. I was there to speak about my plans to focus on 'jobs, jobs, jobs' and encourage domestic tourists back to Central London. As news of my visit spread, a group of residents gathered, wanting to discuss a local LTN. They soon began to interrupt the media interviews I was conducting. This wasn't the end of the world. My team and I moved to the open-air garden at the back of the cafe to conduct our interviews and reduce any inconvenience for the cafe's staff – leaving my deputy mayor, Joanne McCartney, to speak to the campaigners (as the local London Assembly Member, she had far more local knowledge than I did anyway). No problem, we thought. Until I saw the incident being reported as my being 'forced to hole-up inside a coffee shop' to get away from the residents.[10]

The electoral consequences of that protest were negligible, but not every 'vocal minority' issue was as politically harmless. If my great unforced error of the 2016 campaign was pledging to plant a utopic number of trees, in 2021 it was prematurely talking about the 'boundary charge'. This would be a daily £3.50 charge to be applied on trips into Greater London made by non-Londoners. With TfL facing a huge post-pandemic budget deficit due to fares revenue plummeting and inadequate government support, the idea at first seemed like political genius. Even if they didn't like it, those affected had no ability to voice their dissent in the mayoral election: they were non-Londoners. Given this, I was naive enough to mention it in a few interviews in early 2021, before we had worked out its viability.

Big mistake. My opponents immediately labelled the policy 'Checkpoint Chigwell', an attack line made the more irritating by the fact I had to concede it was quite funny. Soon, misleading claims about the charge were circulating online, and it was being incorrectly described as an 'Outer London tax'. Small but vocal drivers' groups, apparently fired up with revolutionary zeal, soon started denouncing the charge with the slogan 'No taxation without representation' – a line I felt made more sense in Boston, USA in 1773 than in Buckinghamshire, UK in 2021. The policy was never even launched, but there's no doubt I lost votes by simply mentioning it.

It didn't help that during the same campaign, I was coming under attack over my environmental policies from a completely different angle. Another 'vocal minority' issue that was constantly raised on social media and by campaign groups was the Silvertown Tunnel, a road tunnel under construction beneath the River Thames between Greenwich to the south and Newham to the north.

I completely understand why, on the face of it, the idea of building a road tunnel is anathema to anyone who cares about cleaning up our air. But the reality isn't so simple. The Blackwall Tunnel – which is the only current alternative in this part of London – was not designed to cope with today's traffic levels. It was opened in 1897 and designed to deal with horses and carriages, even including a bend to stop horses bolting when they first saw sunlight. This Victorian tunnel closes on average around 700 times a year, and a closure for even six minutes quickly leads to a queue extending to three miles. This in turn causes congestion and worse air quality in one of the most deprived parts of London. In fact, one of the most unreliable buses in London is the single decker 108, simply because it has to depend on the Blackwall Tunnel to get from one side of the river to the other. It is under-used as a result: because people opt to drive rather than use infrequent and unreliable public transport.

So, while I understand the opposition, the Silvertown Tunnel is part of the solution, not the problem. And I've spent a lot of the last few years trying to convince people of that.

By the 2021 election, the plans for the Silvertown Tunnel scheme had been around for over a decade. When I had first taken office in 2016, I had conducted my own review into the merits of the scheme and made extensive improvements to make it greener and ensure it provided benefits to the local community. As a result, the scheme was already very different to – and much better than – the original plans. For a start, it now has a much greater focus on public transport, with more frequent, cleaner double-decker buses running from day one of its open-ing. We have also made the construction process greener, facilitating the maximum possible use of the river for transporting construction materials – a way to reduce the number of heavy goods vehicles on the road – and mandating that all vehicles involved in construction must meet the highest emissions standards.

My team and I also decided to keep a close eye on the tunnel's environmental effects – which, due to the

reduced congestion, our models predicted would be positive. TfL has developed comprehensive plans to monitor
the impacts of the scheme on air quality in East London.
At my request, TfL will continue to refresh their assess-
ment as the project progresses, collecting new air-quality
data from 35 sites across five boroughs to do so. Data
from these monitors is being reported regularly through
the London Air Quality Network.

We have ensured the cost to taxpayers, meanwhile,
will be non-existent. The new tunnel will be tolled (as will
be the older Blackwall Tunnel), with both falling under
the extended ULEZ area, thereby helping improve air
quality and reduce carbon emissions. And, because its
construction is being funded by a public–private partnership, neither taxpayers nor TfL had to pay: TfL only
starts contributing money (using revenue generated from
tolls) once the tunnel is up and running in 2025. Indeed,
the toll charges not only repay the construction costs
– they also cover the ongoing operational costs of the
tunnel for 25 years.

All this was complemented by an array of benefits
to the local community. The Silvertown plans include
£1 million to help local businesses plan their travel
effectively and transition to the new charging regime,
and a toll discount available for local people on lower
incomes. And it will bring plenty of jobs to the area:
with 25 per cent of the workforce to be recruited from

nearby, including apprentices who will be paid at least the London Living Wage.

So I was confident that building the new tunnel was the right move. By finally addressing the issue, the tunnel will massively reduce gridlock in the area – which has a negative impact on congestion, air quality and productivity – as well as supporting economic growth in East London.

I had a sense that the local community agreed. As we developed the plans, we held regular community engagement groups on both sides of the river, with the Silvertown Tunnel Implementation Group established to properly scrutinise the project on behalf of Londoners. This democratic scrutiny is at the heart of the whole project: it is written into the planning conditions that we must continue to monitor traffic, air quality, noise, and the economic and social effects for the duration of the project.

And yet for all my efforts to beef up the Silvertown Tunnel's progressive credentials, many environmental activists remained opposed: not least Siân Berry, who was once again the Green Party's mayoral candidate in 2021 – and was a staunch critic of the project throughout the campaign. While I knew that Siân had the best intentions (we had worked together closely thanks to her being a City Hall assembly member), this issue felt like the green movement's very own 'vocal minority' issue: something that almost never came up in conversations with voters in Greenwich and Newham, yet invariably did on certain portions of Twitter and in the media.

As we got into the swing of the 2021 campaign, we encountered a similarly small but vocal opposition to many of our policies, particularly the ones relating to the environment. All the evidence indicated that there was widespread public support for our proposals; yet all of them encountered loud opposition, which was gleefully repeated in large sections of the media. My campaign team were bewildered and frustrated. How had we got to a place where we were spending all of our time defending policies that we knew had widespread public support? And what could we do to get the election campaign back on track?

In 2016, Jack had come up with an innovative campaign idea: that we pay a whistle-stop visit to every London borough over the course of a week. In my previous campaign we'd never quite pulled it off due to the sheer scale of the city and the logistical planning it required. We weren't even sure it was possible without completely derailing all our wider campaign objectives. But in 2021, we were determined. On Friday 30 April, we set off for an intensive week touring the capital.

Spending 14 hours a day speaking to Londoners was more than just a savvy campaign tactic. Getting to speak with and listen to Londoners of all faiths, ages and backgrounds was invaluable. You got a much clearer sense of what really mattered to any given community than you would do otherwise. Quite often, the answer was food. Whether I was making dumplings while speaking to kitchen staff in Chinatown or was being offered kofte and kebabs on a walk down Green Lanes in Haringey, I was reminded that Londoners really like to eat. I ended every day both energised and ravenously hungry. It was the month of Ramadan, and like hundreds of thousands of Londoners across our city, I was fasting every day from dawn to dusk – at that time of year, from about 2.30am to 9pm – so couldn't touch any of the meals I was being offered.

The 32-borough strategy was my attempt to solve the 'vocal minority' issue. The real opinion of London is what I call the pulse, the beating heart of how our city is feeling about any given issue. The only way to find the pulse is by getting out there and listening to what people are telling you – at bus stops, in parks, and in cafes. If you can distinguish real public opinion from the vocal minority – not always easy – then you can get the confidence you need to stick to your guns.

Take my walk along Green Lanes. When I wasn't glaring enviously at anyone eating a kebab, I met local residents who'd been encouraged out of their cars and onto their bikes following a scheme implemented under Streetspace. They loved how London's urban planning had changed since 2020. I later found out that when the council had consulted on the proposals, 85 per cent of respondents had been in support of them.[11] On a visit to a now-pedestrianised Francis Road in Leyton, meanwhile, I met Londoners who had been helped by Cycle Sisters – a group working to encourage Muslim women to cycle, whose twice-weekly cycling trips were going from strength to strength. They too were ecstatic about the changes they were seeing to London's streets.

But you can never really find the pulse of London until polling day. When you start hitting the doorsteps on the morning of the vote, you get an infinitely clearer sense of what the public are really thinking than at any other point in the election. The general election in December 2019 had been heartbreaking in that respect. London has the largest Jewish population in the country, and while I'd had positive conversations with many voters in the run-up to the election, on the day itself it became crystal clear that the criticisms of anti-Semitism in the Labour Party were going to prove catastrophic. We suffered our worst election defeat since 1935. With that experience fresh in our minds, election day 2021 was set to be singularly nerve-wracking. For weeks, we had been facing down media hostility and Tory opposition focused on our green agenda. Had we made the right call?

While I am not superstitious, there is an election-day routine I like to follow. The best-run campaigns have meticulously organised election-day operations. 'Get out the vote' (GOTV) is the pinnacle of a huge amount of campaign work. Activists have worked over weeks, months and years to identify people who have said they will or are likely to vote for your party or candidate, known as 'promises'. GOTV means spending the day phoning or knocking on their doors, often multiple times, to check that they have actually done so. Every door and every minute counts. My job as the candidate was to mobilise volunteers and activists and speak to as many voters as I could.

One of the first places I visited was Islington, in North London. We headed out door-knocking with the local MP and my good friend Emily Thornberry. At one door, I found myself getting into a barney with a local resident, who became verbally and racially abusive. It was a jarring start to the day that left me feeling worried. For a moment. As I walked off, I saw Emily striding across the estate to give the man a piece of her mind. Within minutes she was being supported by residents who were sticking up for my record, and calling out the voter for his comments. A good omen! Londoners clearly preferred me to the racist, at the very least.

Next, on to Crouch End. I was there to pay a by-now-traditional visit to one small business, Dunns Bakery. On election day in 2016, I had discovered that Dunns was running a competition using doughnuts with mayoral candidates' faces on. Whichever doughnut sold the most won. It had taken all of my self-control not to immediately call off Haringey's GOTV operation to send hundreds of Labour activists to buy anthropomorphised

Sadiq doughnuts. In 2021, I was pleased to discover, Sadiq doughnuts were indeed on sale. Another good omen! The me doughnut seemed to be winning.

Finally, after a few hours of door-knocking north of the river, I returned to my home turf. By this time, I was feeling good. Conversations with voters had been positive, and indicated lots of support for Keir Starmer, the new Labour leader. But as every Labour activist worth their salt knows, you never stop campaigning until votes close at 10pm. As darkness fell, I went to the local mosque to open my fast and say the evening Maghrib prayer, before heading on to the famous Tooting curry house, Lahore Karahi, for a quick kebab. The Covid-19 rules meant indoor eating was not allowed – so a friend snapped a photo of me taking my first bite of the day on the street outside and uploaded it to Twitter. Somewhat inexplicably, it went viral. My digital campaigns team couldn't believe that out of all of our carefully planned election-day communications, a spontaneous shot of me having a kebab was the most successful online message of the campaign.

There's a part of Tooting where, for decades, I have spent the last few hours of election day, encouraging every person to use their vote. At ten minutes to ten, I knocked on the door of my final constituent. He had just used our scrappage scheme to buy a new ULEZ-compliant car. A final good omen! Our climate message was landing, it seemed. I knew I could trust the people of Tooting to have my back.

I felt like my pulse-hunting (and omen-hunting) exercise had worked and I was feeling confident. But it was too soon to celebrate.

City Hall was eerily quiet when I arrived to hear the election result the following day, Saturday. Usually, results events feel carnivalesque, with swarms of well-wishers and journalists clamouring to hear the outcome. But due to the Covid rules, there was no crowd this time. That made the mood even tenser than normal. It didn't help that, despite all those good omens, election day had been fraught. Given the record number of candidates, the ballot paper had been split into two sections. My friend Dawn Butler, the MP for Brent Central, had rung me earlier in the day in a panic to say dozens of her constituents had been confused by the ballot paper and how to vote for me. We now had reports coming in thick and fast about a record number of ballots being rejected due to confusion about how to cast your vote. As I sat round with Sarah, Jack, and my senior advisors Felicity Appleby and Njoki Mahiaini, we tried to work out what that might mean for us. They had all been working around the clock for months. We couldn't bear the thought that all our efforts could be derailed by a badly designed ballot paper.

As the count went on, the result announcement was delayed, and then delayed again. At least I'd learned my lesson from 2016: this time I'd brought two emergency

Snickers. As the hours ticked on, I sat in my office feeling the unique combination of exhaustion and adrenaline you only ever get when you are running for election. When the time came to break my fast, I found I wasn't even hungry, and instead relied on drinking some cans of posh Fanta that had appeared from somewhere.

The lights in City Hall are on a timer, and in the evenings switch off automatically to save energy. At one point, the lights went out and I found myself sitting there looking out of my window at the lights across the city, reflecting on the five years that had passed since I was first elected. There was so much more that I wanted to do.

Just before midnight, the call came to go downstairs for the election result. This time the room was more familiar, even if the circumstances were jarringly different. All 20 candidates, in varying states of exhaustion and sobriety, were lined up on socially distant markers on the floor of the City Hall chamber. My mood was different, too. In my tiredness, all I seemed able to think about was the surprising size of Count Binface's head.

First, the returning officer announced to the room what we'd expected: that the two candidates who had got through the first round were me and Shaun Bailey – me with just over a million votes, him with just under 900,000. No surprises there. This was a two-horse race, after all.

But this meant that the second round really mattered.

We required enough second-preference votes to take us over the 50 per cent threshold needed to be elected. As the returning officer started reading out the results from the next round, I stood with a knot in my stomach, wondering if my mental maths would be good enough to work out immediately whether we had made it.

'Sadiq Aman Khan received 192,313 second-preference votes.' Even in my sleep-deprived state, I knew instantly that we had pulled it off. That was over 1.2 million votes in total. We hadn't just won – we had won with the biggest vote a sitting mayor had ever received.

After a short speech and a quick hug from Saadiya and my daughters, I headed back upstairs. My team were euphoric. Following months of working from home in different parts of London, many key members of the team were together again in City Hall for the first time: David, Paddy, Nick, Leah, not to forget my senior advisors Nadeem Javaid and Joy Adeyemo. It meant the mood was extraordinary. We hugged for the first time in ages, having for months only seen one another on Zoom.

All anyone could talk about was the campaign we'd just fought. This had been an election like no other. The unprecedented context and occasional hostility had challenged us all physically, mentally and emotionally. But above all, we felt vindicated. This was an election in which a small group of Londoners had had the loudest voices, meaning a constant war of attrition to get the word out about our climate policies. But we had held our nerve. By doing the hard work of getting out into the capital – and finding the pulse of London – we had figured out what Londoners really wanted: a greener, fairer city for everyone. Now we had another mandate to deliver on cleaning up London's toxic air.

Obstacle 6
Cost

Michael was an electrician. He relied on his diesel van to make a living, using it to transport his tools from job to job. And he was not, I was learning, the biggest fan of my policies.

As a politician, one thing I have learned is that you are never, ever off the clock. I was at my nephew's barbecue in South London, and within minutes of arriving Michael had accosted me just as I'd sat down to eat. As I reluctantly put down the (halal) burger I was eating, I made a mental note to gently chastise my nephew for having invited him. But Michael raised some fair criticisms. Thanks to my policies, from October 2021 onwards he'd be paying an extra £12.50 every day on top of his diesel costs, due to his van not meeting ULEZ standards. He was furious.

I could understand Michael's anger. He had bought his van in good faith just a few years previously, and for as long as he was an electrician he'd have no choice but to use it. Buying a new van was out of the question, particularly as the value of his non-compliant van had now plummeted. That left him having to find an extra £60 every week, while already struggling to make ends meet and support his young family.

Conversations like these are always difficult. I had no intention of backing down on our environmental policies. The second half of 2021 was a crucial moment in our climate battle. In late October, we were planning to expand ULEZ to 18 times its previous size, our key climate pledge from the re-election campaign. What's more, November would bring COP26 in Glasgow, the biggest climate change conference since Paris in 2015. The conference had inspired us to increase our climate ambitions. In September, during a talk at the Barbican Centre, I had outlined our plans for the years ahead, including a new scheme to retrofit homes and workplaces to reduce emissions, and the electrification of our bus fleet.

But none of this would come for free. Climate interventions cost money, and I was acutely aware that that money ultimately came from people like Michael, through taxation. Worse, if we weren't careful, these costs could fall disproportionately on the shoulders of the poorest Londoners. So Michael had a point. If we weren't careful, the green transition would be more expensive than he – and millions of Londoners – could afford.

When I was an MP, I would often tell people that for every stop you took from Westminster Tube station eastwards along the Jubilee line, your life expectancy decreased by almost half a year.

The difference in life expectancy between your average resident of Westminster and of Newham is over four years. The difference between the richest London borough (Kensington and Chelsea) and the poorest (Barking and Dagenham) is five.[1] To me, these are the best statistics to demonstrate quite how unequal London is. As an MP I saw that inequality first-hand. In South London, in the five-minute walk from Ravensbury Road – lined with trees and palatial detached Victorian houses – to the Henry Prince Estate – with entire families living in overcrowded one- or two-bedroom flats – you encounter two worlds that barely interact today, let alone back when I was growing up on the estate.

This inequality is about so much more than just wealth. As ever, climate change is an instructive example. One in ten private cars registered in Kensington and Chelsea is a Range Rover, the highest proportion in the country.[2] Meanwhile, in Barking and Dagenham, less than half of residents own a car at all. Overall, people on lower incomes are significantly less likely to drive polluting vehicles. Only 23 per cent of lower-income Londoners drive a car once a week, compared with 38 per cent overall. This pattern maps onto racial inequality, too. Just 32 per cent of Black, Asian and minority ethnic Londoners – and 27 per cent of Black Londoners – drive a car at least once a week, compared with 41 per cent of white Londoners.[3]

And yet it's the poorest, and often Black, Asian and minority ethnic, Londoners who feel the worst effects of our polluted air. On average, the areas where the most deprived Londoners tend to live have levels of nitrogen dioxide 13 per cent higher than where the least deprived Londoners do.[4] Back when I was a lawyer my team and I would often take on cases of indirect discrimination – where a policy or rule nominally applies to everyone in the same way, but has a worse effect on some people than others. That's just what's happening with the air in London. If you're living in a more deprived area, you're much more likely to experience the negative effects of air pollution.

The pandemic exposed myriad inequalities of this kind. Not only had poorer and Black, Asian and minority ethnic communities been hit hardest in terms of the death-rate, the pandemic had also revealed inequalities that were built into the environment. During the first lockdown in March 2020, I remember coming to realise how important green space was. While I went a bit stir-crazy in lockdown, at least I had a garden. One in five households in London had no access to a private or shared garden during the Covid-19 lockdowns. People from Black, Asian and minority ethnic backgrounds were nearly four times less likely to have access to an outdoor space, be it a garden, patio or balcony.[5]

So by the middle of 2021, when the worst of the pandemic had passed, Londoners were already all too aware of the uneven effects of Coronavirus. And many were understandably worried that when the Covid recovery came, it would only make these inequalities worse – with the well-off benefiting, and the worst-off being left behind.

It was possible to see these concerns developing in real-time, particularly in the months following my re-election in May 2021. As we ramped up our climate ambitions, from ULEZ to bus electrification, we became increasingly aware of a concern that even our supporters were raising: cost. As summer wore on, the news cycle became more and more dominated by the expense of green policies. In July, the Office for Budget Responsibility said the cost of reaching net zero by 2050 – the government's flagship climate commitment – would be £1.4 trillion, of which £350 billion would be paid by the government (and so, in practice, all of us).[6] In January 2022, the management consultancy firm McKinsey would say the global cost would be $275 trillion.[7] Suddenly, the news was awash with aghast headlines about how much net zero would be costing everyone. That autumn, the *Telegraph* ran a piece titled 'The honest green guide' making worrying claims about how everyone in the UK would be footing the bill for green policies.[8]

Articles like these were sometimes a bit galling. They were a useful crutch for politicians and journalists who had spent years denying climate change was a problem at all. They'd realised that approach didn't fly in an age when global heat records were toppling at an unprecedented rate. So they had changed tack: they *were* worried about climate change, of course – they merely had concerns about the cost of doing very much about it.

But admittedly, Britons were right to be concerned about the cost of the green transition. When executed badly, green policies have been known to embed pre-existing inequalities. Research by the UK Energy Research Centre found that the poorest households are not only hit hardest by the government's climate change levy on household bills – they also receive less money back (in the form of home improvements) than they contribute.[9] The Resolution Foundation has found that poorer households are the most likely to live in energy-inefficient homes, meaning they will have to pay a relatively larger sum than wealthier Brits to decarbonise their homes.[10] The public was noticing. By the end of summer 2021, the Conservative chancellor, Rishi Sunak, was being forced to defend his climate policies from claims that they would unfairly burden the poorest.

As these concerns became more and more widespread, my team and I realised we had some thinking to do. We were committed to a green recovery from Covid. But unless we were careful, we knew we could end up making the poorest pay the bill, just as Michael had feared. We realised that not everyone could afford to just throw away their diesel cars: they served as a lifeline to thousands of disabled Londoners, low-income families and small businesses.

To prevent our climate policies exacerbating the

inequality that already plagued London, we needed to take an innovative approach. We would have to draw upon the skills of someone who could see a way through policy problems that nobody else could solve. In short, we needed a visionary.

Fortunately, London has no shortage of those.

A time-honoured tradition: a right-wing MP is on the television, talking about the supposed policy triumphs of the Conservative Party. The presenter, bamboozled by the array of statistics their guest is sprinkling into the conversation, lets them continue unchallenged.

Then, the camera zooms out. There's a third person on the panel: the Italian-American (and Londoner) economist Mariana Mazzucato. She looks unimpressed. Over the next 45 seconds, she politely dismantles the argument made by our right-wing MP with politeness but impeccable rigour. Mazzucato, 1; politician, 0.

There's a reason that *The Times* has called Mazzucato 'the world's scariest economist'.[11] From her base at the Institute for Innovation and Public Purpose at University College London, Mazzucato has spent the last decade unravelling many of the most strongly held beliefs of right-wing economists. No, the state doesn't impede innovation; it drives it. No, the financial sector can't single-handedly drive economic growth; that's not where real value comes from.

It's not just *The Times* that finds Mazzucato intimidating.

One of the first times I met her we were both on the virtual stage at a summit on London's recovery in March 2021. Zooming in from City Hall, I had a relatively plain virtual-office backdrop. Mariana, in contrast, was surrounded by overflowing bookshelves, piles of very important-looking papers, and a giant, stunning artwork of a blue whale. I felt slightly outdone.

We were sharing that stage for a simple reason. It was becoming increasingly clear that City Hall needed Mazzucato's ideas. It wasn't just that her thinking debunked some of the most insidious myths about how the economy worked. It was also that she offered the inspiration we needed to build a better city from the ruins of Covid.

In May 2020 I had joined 46 mayors from around the world in endorsing several principles for cities' sustainable recovery from the pandemic. Mayors from Lima to Sydney had agreed to focus on a healthy, equitable and sustainable recovery that jointly tackled the climate crisis. There would be no return to 'business as usual'. The next month, I had established the London Recovery Board. Co-chaired by me and the then-chair of London Councils, Peter John – later succeeded by Georgia Gould – the purpose of the board was to oversee work focused on the longer-term aspects of London's recovery, including how to grapple with some of the big issues laid bare by Covid-19. The board was supported by a Recovery Taskforce, which would work with local authorities, health and care bodies, business groups, trade unions, the voluntary sector, academia, the national government, police, fire, TfL and more. It was the biggest coming-together of London's institutions in the history of City Hall.

That's where Mazzucato came in. The board's strategy was informed by what Mazzucato called a 'mission approach': that administrations should focus on grand challenges – big, overarching ambitions that everyone could support. Mazzucato argues that these 'missions' are nothing new: they have been used to inspire ambitious policies throughout history. She often uses the 1960s example of NASA's Apollo mission. President John F. Kennedy's aim was simple: to put a man on the moon by the end of the decade. But this wasn't just about space technology. It was also about clothing, materials, communications, and zero-gravity-friendly food. As such, the mission catalysed innovation in various sectors, all brought together by a single big goal: the 'moonshot'.[12]

By September, the London Recovery Board had agreed on nine such missions. It was a wide-ranging strategy, including policies on giving Londoners a 'safety net' in times of hardship, ensuring better access to food across the city, and improving mental health provision. But I was particularly proud of the grand finale, pledge number nine: 'A Green New Deal: Tackle the climate and ecological emergencies and improve air quality by doubling the size of London's green economy by 2030 to accelerate job creation for all.'

I was pleased with the commitment to our Green New Deal. The term harked back to 1930s America, where, amid skyrocketing inequality and economic stagnation, President Franklin Delano Roosevelt had invested in schemes that created new jobs for the worst-off. The New Deal is often hailed as a good example of equitable policymaking, in which the cost burden fell on those most able to pay. Here, too, our focus was on ensuring that the cost of the green transition was spread equitably. The richest would pay more, and the beneficiaries of our new wave of green jobs and public infrastructure would be the most deprived communities. We wouldn't just get London's buildings to net zero emissions, modernise our public transport, and make our city greener – we would do this all while ensuring the costs were spread fairly across society.

In practice, this meant developing policies with three priorities in mind. First, the Green New Deal needed to be democratic. We wanted our approach to be open and accessible. So over the summer, we put details of our proposals on Talk London – an online community where Londoners could have their say on the city's big issues. Talk London didn't always run smoothly. One Londoner drily responded that their '88-year-old, partially sighted mother refuses to swap her wheelchair for a bicycle'. Another suggested I should put my money where my mouth was and become a vegan. But generally it proved invaluable. My City Hall team would offer opinions from the site to help steer policy decisions, and this was particularly true when it came to the Green New Deal. In one month alone, the site received over 68,000 visits, and over 60 organisations attended 'community conversations' sessions. The feedback was profoundly helpful. One user suggested we invest in 'libraries of things' from which people could borrow products like steam cleaners and sewing machines instead of buying new ones. We were soon investigating whether this idea could be rolled out across the capital.

Second, the Green New Deal needed to focus on jobs. Mid-2021 was a dark moment for economies around the world, the point we started to wake up to the scale of the economic crisis that the end of the pandemic could bring. Suddenly, the news was filled with talk of recessions, skyrocketing inflation and mass unemployment. In moments like these, it's tempting to shy away from action on climate – isn't it too expensive to invest in green policies when people are at risk of being made redundant? Our data showed otherwise. In November 2020, my team released new statistics on the status of London's low-carbon and environment sector. It showed that pre-pandemic, the sector was booming, being worth nearly £48 billion in sales, and employing around 317,000 people across nearly 14,000 companies.[13] To our amazement, we discovered that London's green economy was worth more to the city than the construction and manufacturing sectors combined. Putting the environment at the centre of our recovery suddenly seemed like a chance to create thousands of new jobs, not destroy them.

So jobs were at the heart of the Green New Deal: developing them, protecting them, helping Londoners back into them. I knew that our revised city-wide planning document, the 'London Plan' was creating hundreds of jobs through its requirement for all major developments to be zero carbon too. But soon I found myself frantically googling all the environmental jobs in which Londoners might soon find themselves. When, precisely, had my home city become home to so many 'green undertakers'? London seemed to have only one person employed as an 'ethical tea-taster'; might some savvy investment lead to more? And what on earth does a 'bioreactor operator' in a synthetic meat business do, and could it possibly be as sinister as it sounded?

Only when I visited West Acton Primary School in Ealing would I get a marginally less internet-rabbit-hole-induced sense of what green jobs might look like. Rikki and the team from Joju Solar were experts in solar energy, and West Acton was one of 200 schools installing solar panels and other green energy technologies that would provide clean electricity and save an estimated 15 tonnes of carbon each year – the equivalent of around ten return flights from London to San Francisco. The idea had come from one of the teaching staff who, having seen how much they saved on their own energy bills after installing solar panels, wanted to help the school do the same. As I told the assembled teachers, our Green New Deal Fund was investing £10 million in such projects, and its first phase would secure around 1,000 jobs in the green industries for Londoners. All was going swimmingly until I discovered the visit involved scaling a very high ladder onto the school roof. It turns out the only thing worse than vertigo is vertigo with several dozen eight-year-olds laughing at you.

And third, the Green New Deal needed to focus on inequality. None of these policies would deserve the mantle of 'New Deal' if they weren't tackling the inequity that plagues London. So our Covid recovery placed massive emphasis on the 'distributional' effects of our policies – that is, we made sure their costs didn't fall disproportionately on the poorest, but the benefits did.

What did that mean in practice? A good answer came from the Cookbook Edible Library, which I visited in July 2021. The charity Edible London had identified a gap in the support available for worse-off Londoners: while the free-school-meal programme for children offered a lifeline to the poorest families during term-time, there was no equivalent as soon as term ended. Was there a way to get food to these families in the holidays? Yes, thought Edible. The charity specialises in growing food and distributing it to the worst-off families. Nestled at the back of a library in an unassuming building in Tottenham, they had created their own urban farm, overflowing with courgettes, lettuces and tomatoes – and staffed by local volunteers, who cooked the food in a bustling community kitchen next door. The garden was supported by the Grow Back Greener Fund, which offered grants of between £5,000 and £50,000 for projects to improve and create green spaces, green the built environment and help London adapt to climate change. By the end of the year, the initiative had awarded almost £700,000 to 34 community projects to create or improve green spaces across London.

All these measures were our attempt to spread the cost of green policies fairly. But even as we implemented them, we knew they were nothing on our biggest and riskiest policy of all – the one that Michael had been laying into me about at the barbecue just a few months previously. It was time to expand the ULEZ.

On a bitterly cold morning in late October, I made my way to the Queen Elizabeth Olympic Park in East London. It is an unusual part of the city, with wetlands and meadows lying just metres from the towering steel edifices of the West Ham stadium and Anish Kapoor's ArcelorMittal *Orbit*. This was the place where, nine years previously, Londoners from all classes and backgrounds had come together to celebrate everything that made Britain great at the London 2012 Olympic Opening Ceremony. It felt fitting that this would be the place for another momentous moment in the capital's history: the expansion of the ULEZ to cover everywhere within the North and South Circular roads.

But as I approached the Olympic Park, I felt anxious. This was our flagship environmental policy from the

2021 manifesto. But I couldn't stop replaying the conversation I had had with Michael back in the summer. This was an important change, but also a potentially expensive one. If we had got our maths wrong, the burden of cleaning London's air could fall on the most disadvantaged people in the city. As the press began to assemble for the official launch, I felt more and more on edge about what we were doing.

It didn't help that this was perhaps the biggest logistical operation of my mayoralty to date. Since my re-election in May, I'd asked for weekly progress reports, as I had done in the months before the ULEZ had first gone live in 2019. The scheme would involve the transfer of five million individual number plates from the government's Driver and Vehicle Licensing Agency. The largest such scheme in the world, the ULEZ would operate 24 hours a day, every day of the year except Christmas. That would require the processing of millions of images and tens of thousands of payments every day. As I made my way to the meeting point at the centre of the park, I found myself starting to panic. Had we made a terrible mistake?

And then I spoke to Rosamund Adoo-Kissi-Debrah.

By then it was eight years since Rosamund's daughter Ella had died, and ten months since the inquest had formally concluded that her asthma had been exacerbated by London's air pollution. As I approached Rosamund, who was there with her twins, Robert and Sophia, I could feel my anxieties about the policy fading away. Standing alongside Rosamund were some of the campaigners who had joined us on the journey, including 17-year-old Anjali Raman-Middleton, who had gone to school with Ella and had subsequently co-founded the Choked Up campaign for cleaner air. We were there for a formal visit, but it felt like a family reunion. As Rosamund put it, this was not so much a launch as a celebration.

As I chatted to Rosamund and Anjali, I understood that we were doing the right thing. The most disadvantaged people in London – those who lived in inner cities, came from working-class backgrounds, and were disproportionately likely to be ethnic minorities – were the people whom air pollution hurt the most. People just like Ella. Whatever the difficulties, and whatever the cost, expanding the ULEZ was a good policy. We hadn't adopted it because we were ignoring disadvantaged communities. We had adopted it because of them.

I took a moment to think about how much effort we'd put into making the ULEZ expansion fair. Inspired by the Green New Deal approach, we had done everything we could to make sure the people who couldn't otherwise afford to scrap their cars had the resources to do so. We had provided over £60 million in funding for grants for small businesses, charities operating minibuses, and low-income and disabled Londoners to scrap their older, more polluting vehicles. The scrappage scheme would ultimately take 15,500 of the most polluting vehicles off London's roads. And it was working. New data published in October 2021 had revealed that drivers in London were ditching diesel cars six times faster than the rest of the UK.[14]

Despite the sunshine it was freezing, and I had several hours of media interviews ahead. It was going to be exhausting. But at every turn, Rosamund helped remind me why our policy mattered and that we could do even more. 'This is the beginning,' I heard her tell the assembled journalists. 'This needs to be London-wide.' By the end of the day, I was tired and fired up in equal measure. All that remained to be seen was how London would respond.

As I began the journey back to City Hall, I found myself scrolling Twitter to see how the day had been received on social media. I came across a hashtag, #WeLoveULEZ, where parents across London were posting photos of their children walking, cycling or scooting to school. In Herne Hill, South London, a group of parents and their children had decorated a tree with pom-poms, teddy bears and bright Post-it notes to celebrate the new era of clean air.

It felt like we were winning the argument. Yes, climate policies had the potential to be expensive. But done right, they could make everyone better off – and particularly the poorest. Climate action was already improving the lives of people in the most deprived and polluted areas, as well as creating jobs across the capital. I believed it, Rosamund believed it, the parents of Herne Hill believed it.

Eventually, Michael the electrician would believe it too. The next time our paths crossed, I was on my way to see my brother. This time, Michael seemed much happier. With help from our scrappage fund and a small business loan, he'd chosen to invest in an electric vehicle. I sensed that even if I had been eating a (halal) burger, he wouldn't have minded me finishing it. What's more, Michael seemed to have become an unlikely climate change champion: as well as now being an electric-car evangelist, he'd made wider changes in his life, choosing to walk and cycle more and encouraging his family to do the same.

And about time too. Our ambitions to make London greener were about to ramp up even further. Because that autumn, the most important climate conference in history was coming to the UK.

Obstacle 7
Gridlock

I had only been on stage for a few seconds when the pain started.

The date was 10 November 2021, and I was giving a speech before some of the UK's most notable local politicians in Glasgow. The event was organised by UK100, a network of local government leaders that worked to devise and implement plans for the transition to clean energy. It was a friendly crowd, including several UK mayors I knew well – among them Tracy Brabin, Mayor of West Yorkshire; Andy Burnham, Mayor of Manchester; and Steve Rotheram, Mayor of Liverpool. Just a few minutes before, Ali Picton and I had been stood in the crowd discussing whether to include an ill-advised joke about Irn-Bru, Scotland's de facto national soft drink. Like most of Ali's jokes, it was both funny and utterly unusable.

This event was only supposed to be the warm-up act. The next day, I was due to give one of the biggest speeches of my mayoralty, speaking to some of the world's most powerful politicians from the main floor of the most important climate conference in at least half a decade. So I was feeling relaxed as I mounted the stage. After all, this was nothing on what was coming the following afternoon.

Until I started to speak, that was. Out of nowhere, I felt a knot in my chest – a kind of tightening. I started to talk, but everything felt strange. It was surreal: I had my speech typed up in my normal way, and all I had to do was read it – except for some reason I was having trouble getting the words out. I wasn't even sure I could finish my first page.

After two minutes that felt like two hours, I stopped speaking and asked for some water. Ali later told me she thought I'd asked for the water so I could use it as a prop to make that Irn-Bru joke. I wish that had been the case; in fact, I was struggling to stand up. As I took some sips of water, I felt even more awful. I touched my forehead, and discovered it was dripping wet. Feeling weak, I asked for more water, and as Ali handed it over she gestured to me, looking alarmed. I didn't understand what she was saying. I later discovered she had been telling me to get off the stage.

I don't really remember what happened next. As I tried to step away from the lectern, everything went fuzzy. Steve Rotheram and a TfL board colleague, Greg Clark, clocking what was happening, rushed forward, and took an arm each to help me down the steps. As I was carried out into the corridor, I was panicking. In less than 24 hours, I had the biggest gig of my career to date.

And yet here I was, failing to get through a three-page speech to a friendly crowd. It was COP26 in Glasgow, and I seemed to be having a heart attack.

The path that took me to the speech in Glasgow began with a call to Yvonne Aki-Sawyerr, the Mayor of Freetown in Sierra Leone.

In summer 2021, Eric Garcetti had announced he was standing down as Mayor of Los Angeles. This was both good and bad news. The good: Eric's resignation was down to the historic election of Joe Biden the previous year. He had been one of President Biden's earliest supporters for the Democratic presidential nomination, and had been duly rewarded with a high-profile nomination: US ambassador to India. The bad: this development meant Eric would have to step down as chair of C40 Cities.

Since I had been elected mayor in 2016, C40 had been a driving force behind my policies. A global network of almost 100 mayors taking urgent action to confront the climate crisis, C40 represents over 700 million citizens and one-quarter of the global economy. The organisation had been a useful sounding board for many of my most important climate projects. When, in 2018, I declared a climate emergency in London, it was C40 I turned to for an independent review of my Climate Action Plan. When, in 2020, we had decided to build up London's walking and cycling infrastructure to an unprecedented scale, it was C40 we had asked to provide insights from around the world. And when, in 2021, we had begun implementing our strategy for a green pandemic recovery in London, it was C40 principles we had drawn upon.

Above all, C40 had offered a safe space in which to discuss the trials of effecting climate policy on a municipal level. My City Hall colleagues often joked that my meetings with fellow C40 mayors felt like therapy sessions. I recall one half-hour meeting with the Mayor of Bogotá, Claudia López, in which we found that despite being from completely different backgrounds and different continents, the similarities between our two cities' approaches to climate were bizarrely similar (both of us trying to battle through opposition from right-wing national governments; both of us struggling against vocal-minority opposition to our post-pandemic cycling schemes). Through it all, Eric had been at the helm. Without him, I worried that C40 would rapidly become less effective.

The news about Eric was broken to me by my deputy mayor Shirley Rodrigues on a Friday night. The conversation soon turned to who would replace him as chair. There were at least two mayors already in the running. But Shirley had a third option in mind: me.

I confess that I immediately liked the idea. My team and I were well placed. London had helped found the network back in 2005, and since my election in 2016 I'd served as vice chair, helping lead the group in committing to new targets that made cities greener. By that Monday (a day I remember vividly because the previous night, England had lost the Euros final at Wembley on penalties) I found myself getting more and more excited by the prospect. That's when I reached out to Yvonne Aki-Sawyerr for advice.

Yvonne and I had known each other since her election in 2018. Superficially, our cities had very little in common – London the capital of one of the world's richest countries, Freetown the capital of Sierra Leone, one of the most impoverished states in West Africa. Yet I had always found her advice invaluable: she was a straight-shooter who didn't mince her words. Rather than use Teams or Zoom, I'd been asked to call her on her mobile. She told me she was on her way to the airport, having been forced to leave the city due to civil unrest. Assuming it was a bad time, I suggested we reschedule; but in a way I later came to know well, she was utterly unfazed. So, as I sat in my office and Yvonne drove down bumpy roads as her city descended into civil disorder, we had a detailed chat about the most prosaic elements of mayoral politics: how C40 worked, how it didn't work, and how I might run things differently. Yvonne pushed me on my proposed campaign platform, but her advice was clear: go for it.

My conversation with Yvonne helped crystallise why I was so keen to take on the new role. It related to one of the big problems I had encountered as Mayor of

London, particularly when it came to climate policy. Cooperation. Or rather, the lack of it.

Meaningful climate action requires an unusual amount of joined-up global action. At the national level, it is in every state's interests to burn as much fossil fuels for as long as possible – after all, the emissions of a small country like, say, Belgium on global warming will be negligible. The trouble is that, on a global level, this causes disaster. If every nation acts in its own interests simultaneously, then the whole world loses out – global temperatures rocket well above safe levels, and climate breakdown follows. As the influential American ecologist Garrett Hardin famously put it, the environment suffers from a global 'tragedy of the commons'.[1]

The only way to overcome this tragedy is through joined-up global policy initiatives: just like those agreed at Paris in 2015, when the world's biggest economies committed to prevent the global temperature rising more than 1.5 °C above pre-industrial levels. But commitments like these didn't always work out. In the words of the academics Thomas Hale, David Held and Kevin Young, the international system is prone to 'gridlock'. Once-effective institutions now prove unable to grapple with the big problems the world faces.[2]

Take the Paris Agreement. In the years after it was signed, the agreement had taken a beating. First, Donald Trump withdrew the US from the Paris Climate Accords – 'I was elected to represent the citizens of Pittsburgh, not Paris,' as he put it.[3] The situation didn't last; Joe Biden rejoined the Paris Agreement within hours of becoming president in January 2021. But Trump's move did contribute to the larger, second problem: that nations just weren't doing enough to meet their commitments. A UN report published in February 2021 had been damning. Described by UN Secretary-General António Guterres as a 'red alert for our planet', it showed governments being 'nowhere close to the level of ambition needed to limit climate change to 1.5 °C and meet the goals of the Paris Agreement'. Guterres also referred to 2021 as a 'make or break' year.[4]

In standing for chair, I wanted to show that international cooperation was possible. I knew that because I had seen it first-hand at C40. The organisation had managed to get wildly different cities to come together on green investment, for example. Working alongside the Mayor of New York, Bill de Blasio, I set up the C40 Divest/Invest Forum which led cities divesting financial assets from fossil fuel companies and championing investments in the green economy whenever possible – a pledge that 18 cities representing over 50 million people and covering $400 billion in assets had signed up to by the time we reached Glasgow.[5] C40 had also led to a global partnership of 20 world cities who were tackling air pollution in urban centres.

But I thought we could go even further, drawing on many of the lessons we had learned in London and applying them at a global level. When considering whether to run for mayor in 2015, a friend had told me to 'take what you have done in Tooting and apply it to London'. When I asked the same friend for advice about running for chair of C40, she told me: 'Take what you have done in London and apply it to the planet.'

I just had to win round the voters. It was an unusual electorate, small enough that I could speak to every member personally. My constituents were the mayors from the world's biggest cities, coming from across the political spectrum and with all manner of different backgrounds. In the weeks that followed, I spoke to mayors around the globe – often early in the morning and late into the night, given the time differences. I learned about everything from Accra's waste management programme (which led to a 50 per cent reduction in air and water pollution in just two years), to Rio de Janeiro's innovative work to ensure community participation in their Climate Action Plan. It was my first time speaking to some of these mayors. I'll never forget my conversation with the impressive Kate Gallego, mayor of America's hottest city, Phoenix. Towards the end of our call, the conversation drifted towards how our citizens had responded to our climate policies. I was gobsmacked when Kate told me that many of those she represented didn't even believe climate change existed.

By the end of the summer, I was feeling confident. My candidacy for chair had been supported by the mayors of Sydney, Barcelona, Durban, Stockholm, Buenos Aires and many more. I also had the support of current and former chairs of the network including former New York Mayor Mike Bloomberg, Mayor of Paris Anne Hidalgo, and Mayor of Rio Eduardo Paes. In the end, my rival candidates pulled out: the day after the application deadline passed, I received a short email confirming I was the only mayor in the running.

I was excited, but there was no time to rest. This was a rare opportunity to show the world that international cooperation was possible, even – or especially – at the level of municipal government. Fortunately enough, I was imminently going to be given a once-in-a-lifetime chance to prove it. A global forum on climate change, COP26, was coming to the United Kingdom. I was going to be confirmed as the new C40 chair just as the world's leaders arrived in Glasgow.

COP26 had a claim to being the most important climate conference in history. By autumn 2021, all the evidence said that the world was careening towards climate disaster. Countries were being devastated by floods, wildfires were raging, and global temperature records were being shattered with terrifying frequency. Everyone attending thought COP26 might be our last chance to put it right.

The signs weren't good. In the lead-up to the conference, the UK government had largely been missing in action. After the election of President Joe Biden, Boris

Johnson had become more vocal about the need to tackle climate change, appointing Alok Sharma MP as the president of COP 26. But although Sharma had been working incredibly hard trying to get international agreement, to many observers and experts on previous COPs it seemed like the prime minister himself had gone AWOL. My previous COP, in Paris in 2015, had been hyperactively promoted and orchestrated by then-president of France François Hollande. Whereas 100 days before COP 26, protesters were filling London's Parliament Square calling on the prime minister to show some leadership.

In a sense, this presented C40 with an opportunity: to show that international cooperation was possible – just not, perhaps, when Boris Johnson was at the wheel. At our virtual C40 steering committee meeting a few weeks previously, we had discussed who was coming to Glasgow. I was keen for any mayors attending to come via London, so we could spend some time together and I could show them some of our city before travelling to Scotland. Eric Garcetti had made an off-the-cuff remark about how fun it could be if we all travelled from London to Glasgow together; the executive director, Mark Watts, had joked that we could even commandeer a train. Everyone had laughed and the conversation had moved on. Neither of them had bargained on my City Hall team. Three weeks later, some of the world's most influential city leaders were boarding an electric 'Climate Train' in London, to take our COP 26 mayoral delegation to Glasgow. As the train hurtled through the countryside, we didn't waste a minute. After fierce negotiations, Felicity Appleby and Sarah Brown had divided up every minute of my time between their respective fiefdoms: stakeholder relations and media. Every time I wasn't hosting bilateral meetings with mayors, I would sprint down the carriage for another interview.

The closer we got to Glasgow, the more convinced I became that mayors were going to offer the world some tips on breaking the climate gridlock. Even in my most delusional moments – moments Shirley had a knack for talking me down from – I was under no illusions about single-handedly solving this huge problem. But I did reckon that, from our experiences in London and at C40, my team and I had some distinctive insights to offer.

We arrived at Glasgow City Chambers, our base for the next few days, with no time to spare. First up, my team and I ventured to the COP26 Green Zone. We were there to meet some of the winners and finalists of the Earthshot Prize – a global environmental prize set up by the now Prince and Princess of Wales to identify solutions to help repair the planet over the next decade. Every year from 2021 until 2030, the initiative would find and reward inclusive solutions to five Earthshot goals: protect and restore nature; clean our air; revive our oceans; build a waste-free world; and fix our climate. Winners would be selected by the Earthshot Prize

Council, an international team of influential individuals with an eclectic variety of backgrounds, such as Sir David Attenborough, Dr Ngozi Okonjo-Iweala and Shakira. All five winners would receive a £1 million prize fund and tailored support to implement their solutions around the world.

The winners of the Earthshot Prize had been announced at a dazzling awards event earlier in October. There were performances from Ed Sheeran, KSI and Yemi Alade, and Shawn Mendes; Coldplay had put on a show using energy powered by 60 people cycling backstage. The Liverpool striker (and my own personal hero) Mo Salah was there to present one of the prizes. All this meant the prize-winners no doubt had high hopes for the COP 26 presentation. Unfortunately for them, this time the line-up was me, Mike Bloomberg and Boris Johnson. Rather less glamorous, perhaps.

The finalists did a good job of disguising any disappointment at this distinctly more middle-aged roster, however. And for my part, I got to speak to some visionary inventors. It was a 15-year-old finalist, Vinisha Umashankar, who stole the show. Back in her home of Tiruvannamalai, a small temple town in the southern Indian state of Tamil Nadu, she had created a solar-powered alternative to the millions of charcoal-burning clothes-pressing carts that populate the streets of India's cities. Vinisha was astonishing, remarkably self-assured and seeming completely unfazed about her imminent speech on the global COP26 stage. I learned that one of her favourite sayings was: 'Don't watch the clock; do what it does. Keep going.' I resolved to adopt that motto myself.

I felt the Earthshot event hinted at the first way to overcome the problem of climate gridlock. When it comes to international environmental policy, the assumption is that progress will be incremental: after all, it's only the gradual changes that everyone can agree on. This approach is understandable. But there's also a role to play for bigger-picture, moonshot thinking. The Earthshot Prize involved setting huge, ambitious targets and challenging people and institutions to meet them through innovation, Mariana Mazzucato-style. I reckoned that C40 showed that this approach could work for international institutions, too. By the time we reached Glasgow, C40 and our partners had recruited over 1,000 cities to our Race to Zero – a global campaign for a zero-carbon recovery in line with the goals of the Paris Agreement. It was our very own moonshot. What might this kind of moonshot approach look like for the national governments bashing out the COP26 agreement? I wondered.

After meeting the Earthshot Prize-winners, I raced back to the City Chambers where I was due at another event: a keynote speech at C40's flagship COP26 forum. I was due to take on the baton from LA Mayor Eric Garcetti as C40 chair, and share my vision for the weeks and months ahead. It was a big event, and I was feeling nervous. Giving speeches isn't always enjoyable. But as soon as I got up to the podium I knew this was going to be one speech I'd enjoy making. I knew what I wanted to say. It was my chance to offer my second suggestion about how to tackle global gridlock. This wasn't just to be an address about climate change. It was to be an address about climate justice.

I began by talking about our experiences of the Green New Deal in London, focused on creating jobs in the low-carbon sector. At every stage, I argued, we'd wanted to make sure that climate action benefited everyone in society, and particularly the worst-off. The question was: how to apply this equitable approach to climate policy worldwide? My answer lay in focusing C40's policies on climate justice, in much the same way we had focused City Hall's. My first key announcement of the speech was the expansion of C40's Global Green New Deal programme, bringing millions of dollars of additional investment that would double the number of cities working with trade unions, community groups and young people to ensure climate action was in the interests of everyone. My second announcement was bigger: to commit that my first C40 budget would see two-thirds of our total funding allocated to the Global South.

My conversations during the C40 leadership campaign had brought home to me that cities and countries in the Global South – which had for the large part contributed the least to climate change throughout history – were being most severely affected, bearing the brunt of environmental chaos. Over the past 50 years, almost 70 per cent of worldwide deaths caused by climate-related disasters were in the least developed countries.[6] People in low-income countries were at least four times more likely to be displaced by extreme weather, and the UN estimates that in South Asia alone, climate change could push 62 million people below the extreme poverty line by 2030.[7] As C40 chair I wanted to do more to support cities in the developing world facing the worst consequences of climate change.

This was my tentative suggestion about how to overcome the climate impasse. All too often, global talks on climate policy break down because the rich world fails to look out for the interests of the poor. At the 2009 Copenhagen climate conference, rich nations had pledged to channel $100 billion a year to less wealthy nations by 2020 to help them adapt to climate change. But that pledge has yet to be fulfilled, with the UN ultimately recognising that the US$100 billion figure was 'out of reach'.[8] I thought that treating climate justice as an issue of social justice might just help break through this gridlock. When the developed world accepts greater responsibility for the net zero transition – and supports the developing world in adopting green policies – then it becomes possible to cooperate on a global scale.

As I left the conference hall, I felt amazing. London's

approach to climate was getting attention on the world stage. The next day, following a star-studded party in which I failed to land a joke with actor and ULEZ-fan Leonardo DiCaprio ('I would have shared that life raft with you, Leo,' I said. He didn't laugh), my team and I boarded the train from Glasgow back to London. Whatever was happening in the main conference hall, we felt we had communicated what we wanted to: that by aiming high and focusing on climate justice, it might just be possible to tackle global warming collectively.

Until, as the train hurtled through the English countryside, we received one final invitation. To City Hall and C40's surprise, I had been asked to speak on the main plenary stage as part of the first-ever COP26 Cities Day the following Thursday.

My environment team and C40 were delighted. This was unprecedented: I'd be the first mayor to speak in a plenary session like this. There had been some consternation among mayors that cities weren't official participants at COP26; this was a rare chance to show the world why we should be included in future. It was a huge opportunity.

So the following Wednesday, I boarded the train to Glasgow one final time. On the way, my team and I discussed the last point we wanted to communicate. The stakes couldn't have been higher. By then, the rumour was that things were going off the rails in the main conference hall – there was a concern that COP26 was going to end without agreement. Of course, single-handedly my intervention wasn't going to turn that around. But I might at least help change the mood at a conference that was at risk of ending with disappointment. The topic of my session was 'Racing to a Better World', and we decided to focus my words on a third, final message: the value of city-level government in overcoming climate gridlock.

Seeing as we were back in Glasgow, I decided I should show my face at another event taking place in the City Chambers – hosted by UK100 Cities, whom I'd worked closely with for many years. I was feeling relaxed as I took the short walk from my hotel over to the City Chambers in the crisp autumn-evening air. I'd had the time to prepare my speech on the journey, and was looking forward to seeing my fellow attendees. It would be nowhere near as stressful as the huge event I had lined up the following day.

As the speeches began, I was only half paying attention, not least because Ali wouldn't stop talking about her Irn-Bru joke. Before I knew it, the leader of Glasgow City Council, Susan Aitken, was inviting me to take the stage. I walked breezily to the podium, feeling confident in what I was about to say. I stepped up to the lectern and looked around the room at the audience. Steve Rotheram, in his speech, had made a joke about being my 'warm-up act' – I had a quip ready in response. I opened my mouth to speak. And then the tightening in my chest began.

*

By the time Steve and Greg had carried me off the stage, I was barely conscious. Along with my police protection team, the pair helped me out of the room, where I collapsed in a chair by the window to get some much-needed air. By now my shirt was drenched with sweat and I felt like I was on fire.

The fresh air, and some hastily procured chocolate canapés from the organisers, helped me to feel a bit better. But Steve, Greg and Ali were still worried. A first-aider was called. There was talk of an ambulance and oxygen. But I didn't want to make a fuss. After a short while, I felt able to walk and declined the offer of oxygen and an ambulance to take me to hospital. I was relieved to learn that Sarah and Felicity had quickly and deftly dealt with the questions and concerns of the people attending the event.

I felt very tired. Knowing I had a big day ahead, I decided to get room service and go to bed. Ali and one of the sergeants in my police protection team were not happy, and tried to persuade me to go to A&E for a check-up. When I refused, they offered to call a doctor to my room. I told them that was unnecessary. I needed a good night's sleep before my hectic Thursday, and I didn't want to waste everyone's time by going to hospital.

It was only when Saadiya rang that I realised quite how seriously I needed to take the incident. She was extremely worried, having seen a tweet from a local-government journalist at the event that incorrectly said an ambulance had been called. Later I was told that someone else had replied to the tweet, calling the journalist out for being irresponsible and pointing out that my family could have seen it. Well, they had. Saadiya also wanted me checked out. I explained I didn't think hospital was necessary, and I just wanted to sleep, but she wasn't convinced. She explained her worry that something might happen while I was on my own in the hotel room. She asked if anyone could sleep in the room with me, which I suspected was beyond the job description of a protection officer.

By 10pm, I had ordered room service and was getting ready for bed. Little did I know that as I was preparing to go to sleep, a council of war had been formed between Saadiya and Ali, who were plotting over how to get me properly checked out. After trying first to secure a doctor to go to my hotel, and second to persuade me to go to A&E on the advice of NHS Scotland, they'd gone full DEFCON 1 and had called Dr Tom Coffey, my mayoral health advisor. I was just falling asleep when he rang me.

Tom's tone was grave. He told me that he'd seen this happen to a lot of men: after an incident of this kind, they'd gone to bed and had never woken up. He reminded me of a BBC documentary we had both watched about the New Labour years. This was exactly what had happened to the former leader of the Labour Party, John Smith, in 1994; he'd gone to bed not feeling great, and then had a heart attack in the middle of the night and was dead by the morning. I protested that I was a lot younger and fitter than John Smith, but Tom was insistent. 'My advice as a doctor would be, "Go,"' he said. 'My advice as a friend would be, "Please go."'

I rang Ali and told her, 'I give in.' The police protection team scrambled together, and we headed to Glasgow Royal Infirmary A&E. Thankfully it was a quiet evening, and within half an hour I'd had an ECG and a chest X-ray. All seemed well, but I had to wait for the blood tests to come back. When trying to persuade me to get checked out, Ali had told me, 'You'll be back by 1am.' It looked like she wouldn't be too far off the mark.

Then, just before 1am, the doctor told me that one of the levels in my blood was 'borderline'. The issue was a protein called troponin, which is released into the blood after unusual heart activity. I was told I needed to stay in until 3am so they could repeat the blood tests and check the levels again. I wasn't happy but I had no choice. That night I'd planned to do some fine-tuning of my words for the UN panel the next day. Ali had my notes with her. So, in the glaring lights of A&E, we sat there and worked on it. I wanted to leave, but we were all in decent spirits. I was certain that the hospital were being overcautious. The signs were still good: repeating the test was just a formality.

That was, until we got the results of the next blood test back. The on-call doctor told me the troponin level in my blood had doubled. There was a possibility that earlier that evening I'd had a minor heart attack.

I couldn't believe it. I felt fine. They wanted to admit me to a ward, but I refused. I simply didn't believe I had had a heart attack – and I knew once I was admitted it would be a nightmare trying to get discharged. The consultant offered to keep me in A&E as long as I agreed for them to run another set of tests at 6am. If they weren't satisfactory, they would insist on admitting me to the hospital to do a proper analysis, including a CT scan and an angiogram.

The whole situation felt unreal. In a matter of hours I was due to give perhaps the biggest address of my mayoralty. And yet here I was in Glasgow Royal Infirmary, half of my body in suit trousers and the other in a hospital gown, waiting to be told if I was going to be admitted for urgent treatment. It was a long way from being back in the hotel by 1am.

Just after 6am came the results of blood test number three. They showed that my troponin had increased slightly, but not by enough to warrant being admitted, provided I rested and someone kept an eye on me. To my relief, I was given the all-clear to leave if I wanted to. Even though I was exhausted from a night without sleep, I jumped out of the bed. As I left, the doctor advised me to rest and avoid stress that day. 'Of course,' I said.

Ali and I headed back to the hotel. On our way, my phone alarm went off – the aptly titled 'Wake Up' by Arcade Fire. If only. As we had breakfast, Ali's sense of humour was hanging by a thread. When the waiter asked what she wanted, her answer was, 'Eleven cups of coffee.' By that time, everyone else was coming down for breakfast, most of them oblivious to where I'd spent the night. 'You have quite the day ahead – it's the most exciting day in C40's history,' the former Mayor of Toronto and C40 Chair David Miller told me. 'But, David, the last one hasn't ended yet!' I wanted to say.

An hour later, after a quick shower and a change of clothes, we kicked off with some media interviews. I had a daunting agenda: not just the big speech, but also a meeting with the UN Secretary-General António Guterres, whom we had persuaded to meet with a cross-section of mayors from around the world. But through the haze of my tiredness, the day flew by. I remember sitting with dozens of global mayors in a bland meeting room in the depths of the UN secure zone, battling through brain fog, and making the case to the secretary-general about the importance of cities. Guterres ended the meeting by saying, 'Power is never given but taken,' and looking pointedly at me. I had been set a challenge.

Before I knew it, it was time for my big speech. I headed to the COP26 plenary stage. It was an intimidating venue, an enormous hall full of desks with the names and nationalities of over 1,000 delegates and negotiators from every corner of the globe. I wondered whether I was the first person ever to take to the COP main stage who had spent the previous night in A&E, and tried to ignore my tiredness and the knot of nervousness in my stomach. As I took my seat in the front row, I felt so proud of all my team's hard work to get us here, particularly that of my deputy mayor Shirley Rodrigues. Even with a face covering on you could tell she was beaming.

And then it was my turn to speak.

As I walked up to the stage, I felt nervous but assured. I knew what I was there to say.

The problem of climate gridlock was real. But C40 was demonstrating a way through it: by harnessing the power of mayors to change the world. National governments 'can't do it by themselves', I told the hall.

I talked about how when you compare national to city governments over recent years, the difference when it comes to taking bold climate action is striking. It's the difference between delayers and doers.

And I talked about the work we had been doing in London. I told the city's story, and my own. About getting asthma and cleaning up the air. About expanding the ULEZ, launching our Green New Deal, and placing climate justice at the centre of global cities' response to climate change.

As the delegates applauded our policies, I felt my heart swell with pride at all we'd achieved – and hoped that that didn't indicate another imminent heart attack.

The minute I stepped off the stage, I was rushed out of the conference hall and back to the station so we could catch our train back to London. We were cutting it fine, and had to run the last five minutes. It wasn't quite the 'taking it easy' I'd promised the doctor when I'd left the hospital that morning.

Nonetheless, we would soon discover that our message had landed. Forty-eight hours later, I joined members of my team to watch, online, as the COP26 Glasgow Climate Pact agreement was finalised and signed. And there, in writing, it recognised the important role of non-party stakeholders, cities chief among them, in contributing to the objective of the convention and the goals of the Paris Agreement. For the first time, cities were given a formal seat at the table.

In my own small way, I hoped, C40's actions had made a difference. At last, London's climate policies had gone global.

Conclusion
Green Wins

To this day, I remain unable to drink cold milk. At the age of ten, my brothers challenged me to an all-you-can-drink milk competition. In two minutes, I managed to down four pints of the stuff – beating all my brothers by miles. I can still hear the fury in my mum's voice about us wasting two days' worth of milk in 120 seconds.

When you grow up with six brothers and one sister, a competitive streak is fairly inevitable. It was a sense of healthy competition that convinced me to run the London Marathon in 2014 (take that, Ed Balls). It was competition that made me so keen to outdo Zac Goldsmith's supposedly 'green' credentials during the 2016 mayoral election. And it was competitiveness that made me want to stand for C40 chair in 2021. In fact, I'm so competitive that I experience a bout of jealousy whenever my dog, Luna, gets more likes on social media than me (so my daughters allege, anyway).

Above all, I'm competitive when it comes to elections. I believe the Labour Party can make Britain better. But to do that, we need to win. Unfortunately, we haven't always been very good at that.

I learned the consequences of Labour losing elections during my teenage years, when I saw my dad's bus garage closing down, my teachers constantly on strike, and my friends' elder siblings all struggling to find work. That was all a result of Margaret Thatcher's government. And I've experienced the pains of being in opposition, first as a councillor in the Tory Wandsworth council, and then as an opposition MP after 2010. I remember something I was once told by Gordon Brown – who was always very accessible, even as chancellor and as prime minister – over a mug of coffee in the House of Commons tea room, shortly after I was elected to Parliament: 'A day in power is worth more than 5,000 in opposition.'

This obsession with winning means lots of people have been surprised by the effort I've put into climate during my mayoralty. The received wisdom in politics is simple: tough climate policies are a vote-loser.

You can see why people think so. In the 2008 mayoral election, Boris Johnson promised to reverse any extension of the Congestion Charge. Johnson won the election by a tight margin, and many experts said this policy was a factor. In France in 2018, President Emmanuel Macron's planned tax rise on diesel and petrol led to 275,000 citizens protesting through the country. The *gilets jaunes* soon morphed into a wider anti-government movement that played havoc with Macron's administration. Populist parties around the world have since followed suit, using climate change as a wedge issue to divide the public, a strategy visible in the politics of right-wing parties from Germany's Alternative für Deutschland to Finland's Finns Party. A favoured tactic is to cry 'hypocrisy' at every possible opportunity: whenever politicians are 'caught' flying to a climate conference, eating a cheeseburger or travelling by car. In my case, the irony is that it's the toxic rhetoric around this 'hypocrisy' that leaves me little option but to travel in a bullet-proof vehicle when advised. I'd much rather be on my Brompton!

All this means that many politicians are suspicious of tough environmental policies. Everyone acknowledges that politicians should at least mention the climate; but, the theory goes, anyone who is serious about gaining and holding on to power can't place too much emphasis on green issues. You'll be torn to pieces at the slightest sniff of hypocrisy. And you just won't win.

This book has tried to show why this analysis is wrong. I am writing this late one summer evening in the newly relocated City Hall, the greenest City Hall of any global city, watching the sun set over the Royal Docks in East London. From my office window I can see a London transformed by green policies. Even though we're deep in Zone 3, we remain in the expanded Ultra Low Emission Zone. Outside, Londoners relax on the grass in the twilight and swim in the docks: possible in part due to investment from City Hall's Royal Docks team, working in partnership with the local council. When I head home, I'll travel on the new energy-efficient and electricity-powered Elizabeth line.

Then there are the changes you can't see. Since 2016, there has been a 90 per cent reduction in the number of Londoners living in areas that exceed legal limits for nitrogen dioxide. More than 70 per cent of our roads now meet the legal limit for nitrogen dioxide, a 140 per cent increase on when I was first elected. The ULEZ has already been hugely successful in Central and Inner London, helping to reduce roadside pollution levels by 44 per cent in Central London and 20 per cent in Inner London.[1] And, according to C40, we are one of only 30 global cities in which greenhouse gas emissions have peaked. They are currently 33 per cent below 1990 levels.[2]

All this was possible for one reason. We won.

I hope you'll forgive just a little bit of bragging on this point. Because I think it teaches a powerful lesson. A hands-on climate policy need not be political kryptonite, as I once thought. Far from it. You can use climate policy to win elections.

The world today is not the world of ten years ago. Voters care about climate more than they ever have before. The biggest ever opinion poll on climate change found two-thirds of people think it is a 'global emergency', and that number is only going up. Since I was first elected in 2016, the proportion of people 'very worried' or 'extremely worried' about climate change has jumped from about 20 per cent to almost 60 per cent.[3]

So voters don't just need climate action. They want it too. The trick is to deliver environmentalist policies in ways that are appealing to the electorate. That means crafting policies that are not only technocratically competent, but also eye-catching and persuasive. Policies that allow you to govern not just in prose, but in poetry too.

At the time of writing, I have not yet won a major poetry prize. So I'm not self-aggrandising enough to say this book offers all the solutions. But I hope it has offered a few tips to any aspiring green politician. First, we explored why people sometimes switch off from climate issues: whether due to fatalism ('There's nothing anyone can do'), apathy ('This doesn't matter to me') or cynicism ('Politicians are all the same'). The solution is to make climate change – and climate policy – feel relatable to citizens' everyday lives. Tackling pessimism by emphasising the levers we *can* pull to improve the environment. Tackling apathy by showing people how climate change already affects them, their health and the health of their loved ones. And tackling cynicism by adopting a pragmatic approach to coalition-building, and working together with allies from across the political spectrum.

Next, we moved on to the practicalities of governing with a green agenda. We explored the ways climate change tends to get derailed by the managed chaos of life in office: deprioritisation ('Climate isn't urgent, so let's deal with it later'), hostility ('How dare you take away my diesel!') and cost ('I can't afford to go green'). The solution is to place green policies at the heart of your political project, rather than tacking it onto the side. Fending off deprioritisation by reframing moments of crisis as a chance to enact more climate policies, not less. Combating hostility by understanding there can be a vocal minority and getting out there and working out what people really want (or 'finding the pulse', as I call it). And minimising the cost by adopting a Green New Deal approach, which treats climate change as a unique opportunity to build a fairer society with good jobs for all.

Finally, we encountered perhaps the biggest problem of all: gridlock. An effective response to climate change requires global cooperation. But getting rich and poor nations, and left- and right-wing governments, to work together on climate often feels near impossible. This remains an intractable issue. Despite its good intentions, the COP26 Glasgow Climate Pact will probably not meet the scale of the challenge, and national governments may yet prove unable to translate its ideas into practice. My tentative solution is to trust in joined-up global initiatives – initiatives just like C40.

The group has consistently shown that cooperation on climate is possible. Over the last decade, I have spent time with presidents and billionaire businesspeople, UN diplomats and NGO leaders. But the people I find myself most consistently impressed by come from the world of city government. On climate, mayors are leading the way.

In December 2017, I went on a six-day trade mission to India and Pakistan. It was a historic event. We planned to make the first land border crossing from India to Pakistan by a British politician in a generation. But I was just as excited by what I was doing beforehand. On day three of the visit, I was due to meet the Mayor of Bengaluru, R. Sampath Raj, in Delhi to announce a major new C40 initiative.

When I arrived in Delhi, everything and everyone was smothered in a toxic haze. Dense clouds of smog engulfed the city. I learned that some schools had already shut the previous week, with the Delhi government even considering a lockdown to protect citizens from the filthy air.

Our announcement would take place at the Maharaja Agarsain Public School in northern Delhi. Students were taking part in a science class focused on air quality, using sensors to measure pollution levels around their school. Three pupils – Khyati, Shaurya and Harshita – explained how the poor air quality affected their lives. Indian cities faced severe air-quality challenges, especially in winter, when crop-burning and unfavourable weather conditions compounded the existing pollution from transport and power plants.

I could tell. Despite having taken my asthma medication, by the end of the visit I was finding it difficult to catch my breath. Not being able to get enough oxygen not only tires you out physically, it's mentally exhausting too. Our media interviews had first to be delayed and then relocated due to the impact the air was having on my breathing. Simon Harris, ITV London's political correspondent, had travelled with us on the trip and kindly asked if I was okay. I didn't want to talk about it on camera. Not wanting to offend my hosts, I discreetly took another puff on my inhaler and deflected the question.

As I gazed through the smog at the children in the playground, I reflected on the similarities between Delhi and London. Environmental problems – and particularly air pollution – disproportionately affect cities. In both cases, people's health was being undermined by pollution. And in both cases, it had fallen to municipal government to sort the problem out. City mayors are closer to these issues than any other type of political leader.

This proximity to the problem meant that mayors were taking more action than anyone. Before my interviews, I had announced that London and Bengaluru would be leading a new global air-quality partnership network. Sampath and I would co-chair the initiative, collaborating with up to 20 global cities to develop solutions to the international air-pollution crisis. It would involve a major new street-by-street air-quality monitoring system to analyse harmful pollution and explore the effectiveness of new technologies that provided information about the air people were breathing. The findings of the project would be used to improve air quality in almost 100 cities worldwide.

I remember that morning vividly, because it was the first time I realised quite how important mayors were going to become in tackling the climate emergency. Over the next few years, I would discover time and again that cities were bearing the brunt of the climate crisis. And I would discover time and again that the most innovative, effective and radical policies were coming from cities.

I would learn about Dhaka, a city grappling with unprecedented growth due to climate change. On average, 2,000 people move to the city every day, often induced by sea-level rise, cyclones and flooding elsewhere in Bangladesh. The city faces huge challenges: 40 per cent of residents live in informal settlements, mostly with limited access to essential services.[4] The city is rising to the challenge. Dhaka North City Corporation has been working with the national government to improve living conditions in informal areas, including the provision of a more resilient water supply.

I would learn about Accra, where 300 tonnes of waste used to be dumped at illegal sites every day. This waste would often be burnt, leading to pollution in the air and groundwater. The city is responding. In 2016, the authorities launched a programme to give jobs to the informal waste collectors within the city's official waste-management system, and began to close the illegal open-waste sites. Between 2017 and 2019, collection of waste by municipal authorities rose from 28 to 48 per cent.[5]

I would learn about Quezon, a city where almost three million citizens battle with a lack of green space. The city is tackling the problem head-on. The Grow QC programme is repurposing urban spaces to establish community farms for food production, encouraging the use and transformation of idle and open spaces into green and edible spaces. Women in Botocan district have established their own farm and are now growing fresh produce for their families. The programme has helped alleviate the food crises brought about by the pandemic.

And I would learn about New York, perhaps the second greatest metropolis in the world (sorry, New Yorkers). A metropolis which, as the centre of global capitalism, has arguably contributed more to climate change than any other city on earth. The city is taking responsibility. In 2019, New York City Council passed the Climate Mobilization Act, a landmark package of legislation and one of the most ambitious actions taken by any major city to reduce greenhouse gas emissions from existing buildings. The law requires most buildings over 25,000 square feet to meet greenhouse gas emissions limits by 2024, with stricter limits coming into effect in 2030. The

Act is aiming for a reduction of six million tonnes of CO₂e, equivalent to taking a million cars off the road.

I often think back to the book I read before my 2016 election campaign, *If Mayors Ruled the World*. In a small way, they already do.

I bumped into Rosamund Adoo-Kissi-Debrah on a Glasgow train platform during COP26.

A year previously, Rosamund had become a World Health Organization advocate for health and air quality, the first ever such advocate from the UK. She told me she was on her way to hand a petition to COP26 president Alok Sharma, calling for the government to implement legally binding targets on pollution based on WHO standards.

Whenever I see Rosamund, I am reminded not to be complacent.

She is perhaps the least complacent person I've ever met. At the time of COP26, she had spent almost a decade campaigning for new legislation on air quality. She was working with her legal team to explore what a new Clean Air Act (often referred to as 'Ella's Law') could look like. Her life has become dedicated to ensuring that what happened to Ella never happens again.

Rosamund is right not to relax. This book has talked about expanding the ULEZ, and turning London into a National Park City, and building hundreds of miles of new cycle lanes. But it hasn't talked about everything that must still happen if London – and the world – is to meet its climate ambitions.

On my re-election in 2021, I commissioned new independent research into how we can achieve net zero by 2030.[6] It was a stark reminder of how far we still must go. The report showed that the cost of standing still would be far greater than the cost of taking the necessary action to transition to net zero and reduce air pollution. If we don't keep taking action, around half a million Londoners could develop diseases attributable to air pollution over the next 30 years. The cumulative cost to the NHS and the social care system would be around £10.4 billion. It also showed that climate injustice remains a pressing problem. Londoners on lower incomes are still significantly more likely to live in polluted areas than richer ones.

Most worryingly of all, the report showed that London is still at risk of missing its emissions target of net zero by 2030, particularly if we don't receive further government support. Between 2000 and 2018, London achieved a 57 per cent reduction in workplace greenhouse gas emissions, and a 40 per cent reduction in emissions from homes. But we achieved just a 7 per cent reduction in emissions from transport.

We need to go further. And we intend to. We have plans to make public transport better and more appealing, plans for a further £3 million mass-tree-planting initiative, and plans to introduce a new, more comprehensive road-user charging system, to be implemented by the end of the decade at the latest. City Hall's new Rewild London Fund is helping to restore London's most precious wildlife sites and create more natural habitats for plants and animals to thrive. After a 400-year hiatus, we've even welcomed beavers back to London – beginning with the arrival of Justin Beaver and Sigourney Beaver in Enfield's wetlands in 2022.

Yet we're still only in the foothills of the mountain we need to climb. As I write this, I am more than six years into my term as Mayor of London. It has been an exhilarating, chaotic, surreal and dramatic few years. I have run marathons, stood against Britain First and Count Binface, been nuzzled by horses and met activists with a penchant for gluing themselves to City Hall. At times I have felt tired. And at times I have thought about giving up.

In these moments I think about Rosamund, and I think about Ella.

There is so much more that we have to do.

Afterword

I stood backstage at the Southbank Centre and anxiously peeked through the curtain. As Mayor of London, you get used to speaking at events and conferences. But this was the launch of my first book, and the feeling was different. *Breathe* was my personal story in my own words – and in the auditorium there were hundreds of Londoners who'd paid money to hear it. I was nervous.

I've learned a lot about the world of books since this was originally published in May 2023. Like the fact that launch events like this often start with the author reading an extract they've chosen. I'd opted for a section from the beginning about Ella Adoo-Kissi-Debrah, who lost her life to toxic air in London in 2013 when she was just nine years old. But my reading didn't go to plan. After the chair of the Southbank Centre, Misan Harriman, finished his introduction I took a final sip of water, stepped onto the stage, and the shouting began.

'Get Khan out!'

'You're a liar!'

The sad truth is that I wasn't particularly surprised. A small handful of people had been following me around for months and would often shout abuse at events until they were thrown out by security. Tonight, they'd paid around £20 each for the privilege. In fact, as the shouting continued it started to take on a slightly desperate, comic quality; one man had brought a reedy whistle that he kept blowing whenever I opened my mouth. The only thing that did upset me was seeing Ella's mum, Rosamund, in the audience. When I mentioned Ella's death, their shouts of 'It's a lie!' were met by anger from the rest of the crowd.

However, the evening did make me realise that what I'd come to accept as standard was far from it. Rather than only being accompanied by my City Hall team, who like me were accustomed to the continual abuse (and on occasion had been victims of it), this time several of my family and friends were in the audience. One of my brothers was directly threatened with violence. Many of them were horrified and deeply upset. How had this become my 'normal'?

It had begun in earnest the previous year, when City Hall had commissioned and published a new report to look at how the capital could tackle the climate emergency and get to net zero by 2030. It was clear the cost of inaction would be far greater than the cost of transitioning. In response, we announced several policies that could be ready within the next few years to encourage Londoners to shift from polluting cars to electric vehicles, public transport and sustainable active transport. The most significant was extending the Ultra Low Emission Zone to Outer London, so it covered the whole city.

The ULEZ so far had been transformational, reducing harmful pollution levels by almost half in Central London and by 20 per cent in Inner London. But there was still far too much toxic air pollution permanently damaging the health of Londoners and leading to thousands of early deaths every year, with the greatest number of deaths in the outer boroughs. The evidence indicated that expanding the ULEZ London-wide would mean five million more people would be able to breathe cleaner air and live healthier lives. And the public wanted more action, too: in a public consultation which had run between May and July 2022, 59 per cent of respondents had agreed that more needed to be done to tackle toxic air. A YouGov poll had also revealed that nearly twice as many Londoners believed the proposed expansion of the ULEZ should go ahead rather than opposed it.

In weighing up the different options, the rising cost of living was a key consideration. My preference was always going to be for the approach that had the biggest effect on air pollution and the smallest impact on Londoners' wallets. And after seeing the modelled impacts versus the costs, it had been clear that expanding the ULEZ was the best option. I'd outlined our plans to do so in November 2022. Alongside this, I'd announced that we would be introducing our biggest scrappage scheme yet – at that point £110 million – to support Londoners on lower incomes, disabled Londoners, small businesses and charities to scrap or retrofit their non-compliant vehicles. All the money raised by the ULEZ would be pumped back into funding local public transport, including the biggest ever expansion of the bus network in Outer London.

Expanding the ULEZ London-wide was not a simple decision. The easy thing would have been to do nothing and kick the can down the road by suggesting a date for action a long time in the future. But in the end, I knew public health had to come before political expediency. We have too often seen measures to tackle air pollution and the climate crisis delayed (in the UK and around the world) because they're viewed as being too hard or politically inconvenient. But there's no time to waste when people's lives are on the line, and we are facing a climate crisis. The cost of inaction – to our economy, to livelihoods, to the environment, and to the health of Londoners – would be a far too high a price to pay.

I had reached the view that expanding the ULEZ was the right choice for our city and something that would help us to continue building a better, greener, fairer and healthier London for everyone. Yet I don't think I fully realised how tough implementing the policy would prove to be.

Chapter 5 of this book is called 'Hostility'. It speaks to the fact that, despite the majority of the British public viewing climate change as a major issue, you could easily be forgiven for thinking that it was highly divisive, with large segments of the public opposed to strong action. Why? Because, as I have experienced, there has been a small but often very loud group of individuals voicing opinions on the climate that weren't (and aren't) particularly widespread. Brought together with social media, where the algorithms are designed to amplify negative messages, then picked up by the mainstream media, and you have a toxic combination – one that makes politicians get nervous and back down from tough action.

Since this book was first published, this has been the chapter I have lived most days. Radio phone-in interviews were hijacked by a small group of people – the vocal minority – who any time they saw on social media that I'd be on a radio show or broadcast flooded the lines with questions. They also turned up wherever they could – at City Hall, at events I was speaking at across London, and as I said, at the launch of this book.

This I didn't mind. The right to free speech is integral in a democracy. Don't get me wrong, it was tiresome, particularly for Londoners who had given up their time to attend or tune in to an event only to have it taken over by the same small number of people every time. But it was also part of living in a free society.

Yet when police intelligence identified associations between some people in these groups and those on the far right, my staff and the police had to take these concerns seriously. Take People's Question Time, a regular 'town hall'-style event I take part in. In March 2023, the conversation took place in Ealing in West London. There were around 500 people in the audience, around 50 of them anti-ULEZ protesters from across the country. Some of the protesters outside the Town Hall had been seen prior to the event with placards saying the expansion would be an 'end of free movement' and cited a 'UN agenda'. There were Covid-deniers and anti-vaxxers. One placard showed me alongside a swastika, another with a hammer-and-sickle symbol – which did get me wondering what ideology specifically I was being accused of having. One showed a mock coffin with my name on it.

The event was dominated by constant shouting from some of the same group who would later attend the South-bank Centre. But this time, I decided it was important to call this group out. I said that while some people had legitimate objections to the ULEZ, which we would continue to address, some of the protesters outside were part of a far-right group. It didn't go down well with members of the audience, or with the Tory Party politicians present, who had associated themselves with the protesters for their own political purposes. On police advice, once the event was over I was held in the green room for some time; they even had to use a decoy car for my exit.

The next occasion we held People's Question Time the same group of objectors attended again. This time a man yelled that in centuries past I would have been 'hung from the gallows'. Staff members were racially abused, and one person was arrested. It was times like this that I felt for my team: I'd be taken away under police protection while they'd be left to head home on the bus or Tube, and often faced abuse.

Things only got worse from then on. Later, this group started showing up outside my home and targeted my wife and daughters. For several days, a caravan was chained by my home bearing slogans and artwork that included swastikas. A letter came in the mail, addressed to me, with a bullet inside. On one occasion Saadiya and I had been issued with an Osman warning: a serious letter and a briefing in person when there is intelligence of a threat to someone's life, but not enough evidence to justify the police arresting the possible offender.

It was around then that social media about the ULEZ turned toxic, too. Research conducted by the social media analysts Valent concluded that there was evidence of 'an extensive online campaign targeted to undermine support for the Ultra Low Emission Zone (ULEZ)'. It found that 48 per cent of the accounts on Twitter/X mentioning the ULEZ were created after November 2022, and of those, about 90 per cent 'exhibited signs of inauthenticity', using generic names and with a high proportion of fake followers. These accounts – called 'spreaders' – were primarily engaged in retweeting anti-ULEZ opinions from real people or groups opposed to the ULEZ expansion. The aim, the researchers concluded, was to have 'thousands of accounts promoting anti-ULEZ content onto users' timelines'. Valent said it believed the X campaign cost at least £168,000. Where that money had come from was unclear.

As we approached 29 August 2023, when the ULEZ extension would go live, things were reaching fever pitch. But at City Hall we were keeping calm. Having been through both the start of the ULEZ in Central London and then its expansion to Inner London, we'd seen that concerns that peaked pre-implementation were largely based on lack of understanding about the scheme and who was going to need to pay the charge. We knew 9 out of 10 cars were compliant, and that the vast majority of those who thought they were affected would soon realise that they were not.

But I hadn't counted on a Parliamentary by-election. On 12 June 2023, the former mayor and ex-prime minister Boris Johnson resigned from Parliament, and an election was called in Uxbridge for 20 July. I knew immediately what we were in for. In some ways the news was great. The public were sick of Boris Johnson, and from the get-go the Labour Party sent out strong signals that this was a winnable constituency. But we'd never won the seat, not even during Tony Blair's landslide victory in 1997, and it was in a heavily traditionally Tory area of London. I worried that not only would the seat be tricky to win, but also that if we didn't win it, people would blame the ULEZ, and the wrong lessons could be learned.

My team and I offered to help out however we could. I knew the Labour candidate, Danny Beales, who was a Camden councillor and who I anticipated speaking up for the scheme. Yet despite originally supporting the ULEZ, halfway through the campaign the Labour Party decided to disown it, claiming it 'was not the right time' for the expansion. I found myself in an odd position: a Labour mayor supporting a Labour campaign that had disowned one of Labour's key policies in the city. In the hours after voting, despite confident briefing of a successful result from Labour, the Conservatives held the seat by 495 votes, while 893 of the Uxbridge voters voted Green.

I knew the next few days were going to be tough, but I didn't expect things to be as bad as they had turned out. I'd seen the Tory candidate mention ULEZ in his victory speech and had expected some media coverage focusing on my policy, but I hadn't anticipated how intense it would be. I woke up on Friday morning and left the house early as I was due to launch a big anti-misogyny campaign with the comedian Romesh Ranganathan. The first media question asked was about my response to Labour's comments on the Uxbridge by-election.

I knew Keir Starmer, the Labour leader, was committed to cleaning up our air, but as the weekend progressed the news continued to report criticism of the policy from some friends and Labour colleagues. It was a tough few days, and I'll always remember those who got in contact to show support, either publicly or privately. But it wasn't just London and the Labour Party I was worried about. For months, mayors around the world had been telling me that they were watching what happened with the ULEZ: if I was not re-elected following the introduction of the ULEZ they were considering pausing or halting their own ambitious green plans due to perceiving it as electorally toxic. In my more melodramatic moments, I worried that all these very public attacks on the ULEZ endangered the health of city-dwellers, not just in London, but the world over.

From that moment, it was clear that the May 2024 mayoral election would be the fight of our lives. It was always going to be tough because the Conservative government had changed the electoral system to favour themselves: for the first time, it would be a 'first past the post' system. Historically, I had benefited from being Green, Liberal Democrat and other left/centre voters' second preference, whereas this time Londoners would have one vote only, with the candidate with the most votes winning. They had also introduced compulsory photo ID, which disenfranchised some of the people most likely to vote for me – the young, the low-income, and Black, Asian and minority ethnic communities.

My Tory opponent's main pledge was to 'scrap ULEZ on day one', and air quality was at the forefront of the campaign. On one trip to Harrow – I found the borough littered with leaflets claiming I was planning to bring in 'pay-per-mile' road pricing, despite me having repeatedly ruled it out. The irony was – the ULEZ expansion had proved so successful, pay-per-mile was no longer needed.

By the time election day came around, my campaign team were feeling nervous – but also quietly confident. Because in spite of the waves of misinformation, criticism and even abuse, the facts were clear: the action we've taken is working. Since my election as mayor in 2016, overall air pollution concentrations have fallen by 65 per cent in Central London, by 53 per cent in Inner London and by 45 per cent in Outer London. Roadside levels of harmful nitrogen dioxide pollutants were even lower in 2023 than during the pandemic, when our city was in lockdown. Across London, the number of air-quality-monitoring sites showing nitrogen dioxide levels exceeding the UK's legal limits has fallen from 56 in 2016 to 5. And all of this is despite our population having risen by more than a million people.

Election day, Thursday 2 May 2024, was a long day, beginning in the very early hours with an epic thunderstorm. Not a good sign. The rain had stopped by the time I went to vote, and my usual election day routine began – involving, as ever, a trip to Dunns Bakery in Crouch End. This time they'd refused to even make doughnuts featuring my Tory opponent! 42,000 steps later, I headed home to bed in anticipation of an anxious Friday, before heading to City Hall for the results announcement on the Saturday.

As I arrived at City Hall, the sun was shining, and I felt upbeat. Yet I couldn't have anticipated what was about to happen. In the hours that followed, not only was history made by Londoners electing a mayor for the third consecutive time, but it was a landslide victory. The overall result saw an unprecedented swing in the vote towards me, with the total vote being the second largest in UK electoral history. (I'll forgive the person who holds the top spot – me in the 2016 mayoral election!) And another reason to love London: Count Binface comfortably beat the far right, Britain First.

But the biggest achievement of all? That I am sitting here as mayor with millions of Londoners breathing cleaner air. As I write, I'm on my way to Rome at the invitation of The Pope – to speak at a conference organised by the Vatican about how to tackle climate change.

London truly has sent a message to the world. Talking about the climate and taking bold action is not a political death wish. You can use climate policy to win elections. And London's story, this story – my story – reveals how.

Acknowledgements

The journey to becoming mayor of my home city has been a rollercoaster, encompassing three parliamentary elections in a marginal seat, a Labour selection against some formidable opponents, and then two intense mayoral elections. Without my brilliant campaign teams and volunteers – first in Tooting and then across our city – I wouldn't be mayor of the greatest city in the world, able to implement the changes I have described in this book.

When I left the legal profession for politics, and was elected as the MP for Tooting, I started with a team of four people. That number had grown to twenty by the mayoral candidate selection, and doubled again during the election itself. And then I arrived at City Hall. That first day, as I addressed people from the ground floor of our nine-storey building, looking up to the hundreds of staff congregated on the levels above, I recall thinking 'that escalated quickly'. While I had a good idea of what I wanted to achieve as mayor, I hadn't expected or anticipated the wealth of talent that was waiting for me at City Hall. Special thanks must go to all my Deputy Mayors; when it comes to climate, Shirley Rodrigues, Val Shawcross, Heidi Alexander and Seb Dance have played a particularly crucial role in changing our city forever. The level of skill, expertise and innovation demonstrated by the staff at Transport for London in putting our climate policies into practice shows why our transport system is envied across the world. London government is blessed with sadly too many unsung heroes to mention here – but I must thank Elliot Treharne from City Hall for his passion, commitment, and unique ability to bring the technical minutiae of briefing papers to life. Shirley and Elliot: your work has saved lives.

Over the years, many colleagues have become my best friends, and I am thankful not only for the talent they have brought to our capital, but for the love and warmth shown by my senior teams both before and since coming to City Hall. My Chief of Staff David Bellamy was at the vanguard of what I refer to as my 'Day One' team and deserves real credit for his immeasurable service to our city. I am especially grateful to both my former senior top team – Nick Bowes, Paddy Hennessy, Leah Kreitzman and Jack Stenner – and current senior top team – Felicity Appleby, Sarah Brown and Richard Watts. Joy Adeyemo and Nadeem Javaid are two further 'Day Ones' without whose invaluable support and guidance I would be lost. In addition to being an integral part of my City Hall team, Sarah Coombes' advice and insight in regard to this book has been of great value.

This book was a labour of love written outside work hours. Someone there by my side throughout, as she has been for the past decade, was Ali Picton. This book would simply not have been written without her. I am grateful for the conversations, texts and emails, often late into the night and over the weekends. Her work ethic has kept me on my toes and her dry humour has kept me sane.

As I have explained in this book, climate change is an issue I came to relatively late. Many politicians blazed a trail well before me – none more so than my good friend Ed Miliband MP. Over the years I have met many inspiring climate campaigners from all walks of life. Mike Bloomberg continues to effect tangible and world-leading change in this area, as do my fellow mayors from across the globe, many of whom I mention in the book. Perhaps most encouraging are the younger activists I have met – from Vanessa Nakate to Hilda Flavia Nakabuye. I want to pay special tribute to Rosamund Kissi-Debrah, Sophia and Robert Kissi-Debrah, Jenny Bates, Anna Beech, Siân Berry, Simon Birkett, Jane Burston, Jocelyn Cockburn, Dr Tom Coffey, Dr Gary Fuller, Baroness Jenny Jones, Professor Frank Kelly, Professor Kevin Fenton, Andrea Lee, Oli Lord, Martin Machray, Anjali Raman-Middleton, Professor Jonathan Grigg, Professor Stephen Holgate, Dr Maria Neira, Caroline Russell, Ashok Sinha, Dr Colin Wallis, Mark Watts, Sarah Woolnough, Jemima Hartshorn.

As a politician, when you commit to attending a dinner, and then find yourself sitting next to someone you don't know too well, it can be a bit of a gamble. You can often be resigned to either a very dull evening, or a fascinating one. Luckily when I found myself sitting next to Jonny Geller at an event a couple of years ago, my experience was very much the latter, and it has been a pleasure to be represented by Jonny and his agency, Curtis Brown, in the publication of this book. The fact I can say I share an agent with Bono only played a small part in this decision, I promise. The entire team at Curtis Brown, including Ciara Finan and Viola Hayden, deserve many thanks for their role in bringing this book to fruition.

I was on the train to COP26 in Glasgow when I received a text from Jonny telling me that Helen Conford at Hutchinson Heinemann was interested in the book and keen to know more. As a longstanding climate change champion herself, I couldn't think of a better publisher for this book, and I am particularly grateful for her guidance on the early draft. The arrival of Rowan Borchers as the book's editor was a gamechanger: it wouldn't be what it is without his honest critique, literary talent and political judgement. The entire team at Penguin Random House deserves huge credit, with special thanks to Olivia Allen, Meredith Benson, Alice Brett, Najma Finlay, Ania Gordon, Laurie Ip Fung Chun, Isabelle Ralphs, Jason Smith, Mat Watterson and Lydia Weigel.

Finally, and most importantly, thank you to my family. I am lucky to have the best brothers and sister anyone could hope for. We lost our wonderful dad too soon, but we are blessed to have our mum and her wonderful daughters-in-law and fantastic grandkids. To my in-laws: thank you for always being so supportive. I hope you don't regret Saadiya choosing me all those years ago!

To my wife Saadiya: without you I wouldn't be where I am today. Your love, encouragement and understanding makes me the man I am, and the man I want to be. I love you. To my daughters Anisah and Ammarah: the overriding reason I care about tackling the climate crisis is because we can either be the last generation to not 'get it', or the first generation to really understand and act. I know having me as your dad isn't always easy. The arguments I have set out in this book are because I want to create a better future for the next generation – so this book is for you.

Notes

Introduction: Ella's Story

1 Rootman, L., Saynor, E., and Mahmood, K., 'Air Quality –
  High Court Order for an inquest to be re-heard to consider
  impact of air pollution', CMS Cameron McKenna Nabarro
  Olswang LLP, 14 January 2020: https://www.lexology.com/
  library/detail.aspx?g=d82592f0-a5fa-478c-a8aa-cdec7b766d9f

2 Marshall, C., 'Illegal levels of air pollution linked to child's
  death', BBC News, 3 July 2018: https://www.bbc.co.uk/news/
  science-environment-44612642

3 Kissi-Debrah, R., 'Air pollution killed my daughter – and
  now I can prove it', *Guardian*, 31 August 2018: https://
  www.theguardian.com/commentisfree/2018/aug/31/
  proof-air-pollution-killed-my-daughter-ella-new-inquest

4 World Health Organization, 'Billions of people still breathe
  unhealthy air: new WHO data', 4 April 2022: https://www.
  who.int/news/item/04-04-2022-billions-of-people-still-
  breathe-unhealthy-air-new-who-data

5 Fuller, R., Landrigan, P. J., Balakrishnan, K., Bathan, G.,
  et al., 'Pollution and health: a progress update', *Lancet* 6(6),
  1 June 2022: https://www.thelancet.com/journals/lanplh/
  article/PIIS2542-5196(22)00090-0/fulltext

6 World Health Organization, 'WHO releases country estimates
  on air pollution exposure and health impact', 27 September 2016:
  https://www.who.int/news/item/27-09-2016-who-releases-
  country-estimates-on-air-pollution-exposure-and-health-impact

7 Perera, F., 'Pollution from Fossil-Fuel Combustion is the Leading Environmental Threat to Global Pediatric Health and Equity: Solutions Exist', *International Journal of Environmental Research and Public Health* 15(1), January 2018: https://www.ncbi.nlm.nih.gov/pmc/articles/PMC5800116

Obstacle 1: Fatalism

1 HM Treasury, 'Public spending statistics: February 2022', 25 February 2022: https://www.gov.uk/government/statistics/public-spending-statistics-release-february-2022/public-spending-statistics-february-2022

2 Mulholland, H., 'Boris Johnson raises doubts over government's deficit reduction plan', *Guardian*, 6 September 2010: https://www.theguardian.com/politics/2010/sep/06/boris-johnson-doubts-deficit-reduction

3 'C-charge zone's scrapping "is right" – Boris Johnson', BBC News, 22 December 2010: https://www.bbc.co.uk/news/mobile/uk-england-london-12064577; Johnson, B., 'Keep on truckin', folks – you've already won', *Telegraph*, 2 November 2000: https://www.telegraph.co.uk/comment/4256411/Keep-on-truckin-folks-youve-already-won.html; Johnson, B., 'I can't stand this December heat, but it has nothing to do with global warming', *Telegraph*, 20 December 2015: https://www.telegraph.co.uk/news/weather/12060976/I-cant-stand-this-December-heat-but-it-has-nothing-to-do-with-global-warming.html

4 'Environmental Pessimism in Britain', Redfield & Wilton Strategies, 10 August 2022: https://redfieldandwiltonstrategies.com/environmental-pessimism-in-britain

5 'Climate fatalism grips young people worldwide while the urgency for solution-oriented media grows', Ipsos, 10 November

2021: https://www.ipsos.com/en-uk/climate-fatalism-grips-young-people-worldwide-while-urgency-solution-oriented-media-grows

6 Barber, B. R., *If Mayors Ruled the World: Dysfunctional Nations, Rising Cities* (Yale University Press, 2013)

7 Ibid.

8 Barber, B. R., 'Dysfunctional Nations, Rising Cities', *Huff-Post*, 1 November 2013: https://www.huffpost.com/entry/dysfunctional-nations_b_4192366

9 OECD, 'Building Trust in Public Institutions: Building Trust to Reinforce Democracy: Key Findings from the 2021 OECD Survey on Drivers of Trust in Public Institutions', 9 June 2022: https://www.oecd.org/governance/trust-in-government

10 Clark, T., 'London offers Labour chance of big gains at general election, says poll', *Guardian*, 27 March 2015: https://www.theguardian.com/politics/2015/mar/27/london-labour-gains-general-election-poll

11 Goldsmith, Z., 'On Thursday, are we really going to hand the world's greatest city to a Labour party that thinks terrorists is its friends?', *Mail on Sunday*, 1 May 2016: https://www.dailymail.co.uk/debate/article-3567537/On-Thursday-really-going-hand-world-s-greatest-city-Labour-party-thinks-terrorists-friends-passionate-plea-ZAC-GOLDSMITH-four-days-Mayoral-election.html

Obstacle 2: Apathy

1 YouGov/Mayor of London Survey Results: 21–24 November 2016

2 Mortimer, C., 'Boris Johnson accused of burying report on the number of deprived schools in London's most polluted areas', *Independent*, 16 May 2016: https://www.

independent.co.uk/climate-change/news/boris-johnson-accused-of-burying-report-on-the-number-of-deprived-schools-in-london-s-most-polluted-areas-a7033016.html

3 Mayor of London, 'Hundreds of London schools exceed legal air quality levels', 1 July 2016: https://www.london.gov.uk/press-releases/mayoral/hundreds-of-schools-exceed-air-quality-limits

4 Harvard Thinks Big, 'Daniel Gilbert – "Global Warming and Psychology"', 21 March 2010: https://vimeo.com/10324258

5 Maume, C., 'Tony Benn, James Rebhorn and the rise of the "selfie" obituary', *Independent*, 26 March 2014: https://www.independent.co.uk/news/people/the-rise-of-the-selfie-obituary-9215250.html

6 Kolbert, E., 'Postscript: Mario Cuomo (1932–2015)', NewYorker.com, 1 January 2015: https://www.newyorker.com/news/news-desk/postscript-mario-cuomo

7 Mayor of London, 'Air quality alerts to warn Londoners about air pollution', 4 August 2016: https://www.london.gov.uk/press-releases/mayoral/air-quality-alerts-warn-londoners-about-pollution

Obstacle 3: Cynicism

1 Quilter-Pinner, H., Statham, R., Jennings, W., and Valgarðsson, V., *Trust Issues: Dealing with Distrust in Politics*, Institute for Public Policy Research, December 2021: https://www.ippr.org/research/publications/trust-issues

2 Heydecker, R., Ormston, H., and Wallace, J., *GDWe: A Spotlight on Democratic Wellbeing*, Carnegie UK, January 2022: https://www.carnegieuktrust.org.uk/publications/gdwe-a-spotlight-on-democratic-wellbeing

3 'Three-quarters of adults in Great Britain worry about climate change', Office for National Statistics, 5 November 2021:

https://www.ons.gov.uk/peoplepopulationandcommunity/
wellbeing/articles/threequartersofadultsingreatbritainworry
aboutclimatechange/2021-11-05

4 'Reducing carbon emissions and tackling climate change: 2021–2022 EIB Climate Survey, part 1 of 3', European Investment Bank: https://www.eib.org/en/surveys/climate-survey/ 4th-climate-survey/skepticism-reduced-carbon-emission-targets.htm

Obstacle 4: Deprioritisation

1 Mason, R., 'David Cameron at centre of "get rid of all the green crap" storm', *Guardian*, 21 November 2013: https://www.theguardian.com/environment/2013/nov/21/david-cameron-green-crap-comments-storm

2 Brown, R., 'Funding London's transport in the aftermath of coronavirus', Centre for London, 30 March 2020: https://www.centreforlondon.org/blog/funding-london-transport

3 Aitkenhead, D., 'Interview: Sadiq Khan on his struggles during lockdown in London', *The Times*, 20 June 2020: https://www.thetimes.co.uk/article/interview-sadiq-khan-on-his-struggles-during-lockdown-in-london-8msxmord2

4 Allam, Z., Bibri, S. E., Chabaud, D., and Moreno, C., 'The "15-Minute City" concept can shape a net-zero urban future', *Nature*, 8 April 2022: https://www.nature.com/articles/s41599-022-01145-0

5 'New TfL data shows significant increase in walking and cycling since the pandemic started', Transport for London, 14 December 2022: https://tfl.gov.uk/info-for/media/press-releases/2020/december/new-tfl-data-shows-significant-increase-in-walking-and-cycling-since-the-pandemic-started

6 Ibid.

7 Mayor of London, 'Mayor hails success of School Streets programme', 10 March 2022: https://www.london.gov.uk/press-releases/mayoral/mayor-hails-success-of-schools-streets-programme

8 Bosetti, N., Connelly, K., Harding, C., and Rowe, D., *Street Shift: The Future of Low-Traffic Neighbourhoods*, Centre for London, June 2022: https://www.centreforlondon.org/wp-content/uploads/2022/06/CFL-StreetShift-LTNs-Final.pdf

9 'New TfL data shows significant increase in walking and cycling since the pandemic started': https://tfl.gov.uk/info-for/media/press-releases/2020/december/new-tfl-data-shows-significant-increase-in-walking-and-cycling-since-the-pandemic-started

10 Carrington, D., '"Dramatic" plunge in London air pollution since 2016, report finds', *Guardian*, 3 October 2020: https://www.theguardian.com/environment/2020/oct/03/dramatic-plunge-in-london-air-pollution-since-2016-report-finds

11 London Councils, '2020 Air Quality Public Polling': https://www.londoncouncils.gov.uk/our-key-themes/environment/air-quality-london/air-quality-public-polling

12 Transport and Environment, 'Nearly 9 in 10 Londoners want cars to give way to bikes, buses and walking to tackle urban air pollution', 11 June 2020: https://www.transportenvironment.org/discover/nearly-9-10-londoners-want-cars-give-way-bikes-buses-and-walking-tackle-urban-air-pollution

Obstacle 5: Hostility

1 Nixon, R. M., 'The Great Silent Majority', delivered 3 November 1969: https://www.americanrhetoric.com/speeches/richardnixongreatsilentmajority.html

2 London Councils, 'Londoners' views of climate change in 2021':
   https://www.londoncouncils.gov.uk/climate-change-poll

3 *Daily Mail*, 19 July 2022: https://www.pressreader.com/uk/
   daily-mail/20220719/281818582560094

4 Whale, J., 'We need cool heads instead of the hot air',
   Daily Express, 18 July 2022: https://www.express.co.uk/
   comment/expresscomment/1642262/heatwave-climate-
   change-schools-extinction-rebellion

5 O'Neill, B., 'The heatwave green hysteria is out of control',
   Spectator, 18 July 2022: https://www.spectator.co.uk/article/
   the-heatwave-green-hysteria-is-out-of-control

6 'Majority of Londoners Support Pedestrianisation of London,
   but Find Policies So Far Ineffective', Redfield & Wilton Strategies, 21 October 2020: https://redfieldandwiltonstrategies.com/
   majority-of-londoners-support-pedestrianisation-of-london-but-
   find-policies-so-far-ineffective

7 Scully, E., 'London goes to WAR with Sadiq's "illegal" road
   schemes: Residents in five boroughs take fight to High Court
   over cycle-friendly "Low Traffic Neighbourhoods" set up in
   lockdown', *Daily Mail*, 22 January 2021: https://www.dailymail.
   co.uk/news/article-9176891/London-goes-WAR-Sadiqs-
   illegal-road-schemes.html

8 Martin, H., 'Low-traffic neighbourhoods make air pollution WORSE: Report reveals toxic nitrogen dioxide levels
   rose when council closed 11 south London streets', *Daily
   Mail*, 6 December 2020: https://www.dailymail.co.uk/news/
   article-9023187/Low-traffic-neighbourhoods-make-air-
   pollution-WORSE-report-reveals.html

9 Laker, L., 'London mayoral election: which candidate is best
   for cycling?', *Guardian*, 4 May 2021: https://www.theguardian.
   com/environment/bike-blog/2021/may/04/london-mayoral-
   election-which-candidate-is-best-for-cycling?CMP=
   twt_a-environment_b-gdneco

10 Lydall, R., 'London Mayoral campaign: Sadiq Khan forced to hole-up inside coffee shop after protesters turn up at launch', *Evening Standard*, 4 March 2021: https://www.standard.co.uk/news/mayor/sadiq-khan-cafe-london-mayoral-race-launch-shaun-bailey-b922137.html

11 Hackney Council, 'Green Lanes Cycle Scheme' proposal: https://rebuildingagreenerhackney.commonplace.is/proposals/green-lanes-cycle-scheme

Obstacle 6: Cost

1 Trust for London, 'Life expectancy by London borough': https://www.trustforlondon.org.uk/data/life-expectancy-borough

2 Willmoth, H., 'Kensington and Chelsea buys more SUVs than anywhere else in the UK', SWLondoner, 25 October 2021: https://www.swlondoner.co.uk/news/25102021-kensington-and-chelsea-buys-more-suvs-than-anywhere-else-in-the-uk

3 *Health Impacts of Cars in London*, Greater London Authority, September 2015: https://www.london.gov.uk/sites/default/files/health_impact_of_cars_in_london-sept_2015_final_0.pdf

4 Williamson, T., Nunn, J., and Pearce, H., *Air Pollution and Inequalities in London: 2019 Update*, Logika Noise Air Quality Consultants, 12 October 2021: https://www.london.gov.uk/sites/default/files/air_pollution_and_inequalities_in_london_2019_update_0.pdf

5 'One in eight British households has no garden', Office for National Statistics, 14 May 2020: https://www.ons.gov.uk/economy/environmentalaccounts/articles/oneineightbritishhouseholdshasnogarden/2020-05-14

6 Office for Budget Responsibility, *Fiscal Risks Report*, July 2021: https://obr.uk/docs/dlm_uploads/Fiscal_risks_report_July_2021.pdf

7 'The net-zero transition: What it would cost, what it could bring', McKinsey Sustainability: https://www.mckinsey.com/business-functions/sustainability/our-insights/the-net-zero-transition-what-it-would-cost-what-it-could-bring

8 Shute, J., 'The honest green guide: what "net zero" will really cost you', *Telegraph*, 23 October 2021: https://www.telegraph.co.uk/news/2021/10/23/honest-green-guide-net-zero-will-really-cost

9 Barrett, J., Owen, A., and Taylor, P., *Funding a Low Carbon Energy System: a fairer approach?*, UK Energy Research Centre 2018: https://d2e1qxpsswcpgz.cloudfront.net/uploads/2020/03/ukerc_funding_a_low_cost_energy_system.pdf

10 'Costs of Net Zero transition for low-and-middle income households must be addressed, rather than used to derail decarbonisation', Resolution Foundation, 30 September 2021: https://www.resolutionfoundation.org/press-releases/costs-of-net-zero-transition-for-low-and-middle-income-households-must-be-addressed-rather-than-used-to-derail-decarbonisation

11 Rumbelow, H., 'Don't mess with Mariana Mazzucato, the world's scariest economist', *The Times*, 7 November 2017: https://www.thetimes.co.uk/article/dont-mess-with-mariana-mazzucato-the-worlds-scariest-economist-7xs6qlxpx

12 Mazzucato, M., and Dibb, G., *Missions: A Beginner's Guide*, UCL Institute for Innovation and Public Purpose (2019): https://www.ucl.ac.uk/bartlett/public-purpose/sites/public-purpose/files/iipp_policy_brief_09_missions_a_beginners_guide.pdf

13 'London's Low Carbon and Environmental Goods and Services Sector. Extract from Monthly Dataset for 2019 and 2020', kMatrix Data Services, November 2020: https://www.london.gov.uk/sites/default/files/lcegs-2019-20_update-final-final-181120.pdf

14 CleanCities, 'Londoners ditch dirty diesel ahead of ULEZ expansion', 22 October 2021: https://cleancitiescampaign. org/ulez-londoners-ditch-dirty-diesel

Obstacle 7: Gridlock

1 Hardin, G., 'The Tragedy of the Commons', *Science* 162(3859), 13 December 1968 (pp. 1243–8): https://www.jstor.org/ stable/1724745

2 Hale, T., Held, D., and Young, K., *Gridlock: Why Global Cooperation Is Failing When We Need It Most* (Polity, 2013)

3 Gambino, L., 'Pittsburgh fires back at Trump: we stand with Paris, not you', *Guardian*, 1 June 2017: https://www. theguardian.com/us-news/2017/jun/01/pittsburgh-fires-back-trump-paris-agreement

4 'UN climate report a "red alert" for the planet: Guterres', UN News, 26 February 2021: https://news.un.org/en/ story/2021/02/1085812

5 'Ahead of COP26, Six Additional Cities Pledge to Divest From Fossil Fuel Companies and Invest in Climate Solutions', C40 Cities, 26 October 2021: https://www.c40.org/news/ cop26-cities-divest-fossil-fuels-invest-solutions

6 More, C. H., Swaby, G. S. A., and Wangdi, S. P., *Time to Redress the Globally Unjust Cost of Climate Change*, International Institute for Environment and Development, September 2019: https:// pubs.iied.org/17726iied

7 UN Humanitarian, *Why the Climate Crisis Is a Humanitarian Emergency*, United Nations Office for the Coordination of Humanitarian Affairs, 27 January 2021: https://unocha. exposure.co/why-the-climate-crisis-is-a-humanitarian-emergency

8 Timperley, J., 'The broken $100-billion promise of climate finance – and how to fix it', *Nature*, 20 October 2021: https://www.nature.com/articles/d41586-021-02846-3

Conclusion: Green Wins

1 Mayor of London, 'Ultra Low Emission Zone will be expanded London-wide', 25 November 2022: https://www.london.gov.uk/ultra-low-emission-zone-will-be-expanded-london-wide

2 '30 of the world's largest and most influential cities have peaked greenhouse gas emissions', C40 Cities, 8 October 2019: https://www.c40.org/news/30-of-the-world-s-largest-most-influential-cities-have-peaked-greenhouse-gas-emissions

3 Akehurst, S., 'Why no climate culture war in the UK?', Strong Message Here, 16 September 2021: https://strongmessage-here.substack.com/p/why-no-climate-culture-war-in-the

4 Arias-Granada, Y., Haque, S. S., Joseph, G., and Yanez-Pagans, M., *Water and Sanitation in Dhaka Slums: Access Quality, and Informality in Service Provision*, World Bank Group (August 2018): https://documents1.worldbank.org/curated/en/607511534337128809/pdf/WPS8552.pdf

5 'Cities100: Recognition and inclusion of informal waste collectors reaps large benefits in Accra', C40 Knowledge, October 2019: https://www.c40 knowledgehub.org/s/article/Cities100-Recognition-and-inclusion-of-informal-waste-collectors-reaps-large-benefits-in-Accra?language=en_US

6 Mayor of London, 'Pathways to net zero carbon by 2030': https://www.london.gov.uk/what-we-do/environment/climate-change/zero-carbon-london/pathways-net-zero-carbon-2030

Index

ABOUT THE AUTHOR

Sadiq Khan is the Mayor of London. Born and raised in Tooting, he began his career as a human rights lawyer before being elected to parliament in 2005. A former Cabinet Minister, Sadiq became passionate about air quality and climate change after developing asthma while training for the 2014 London Marathon. Since then, he has been on a mission to make London greener and healthier.

He was elected mayor in 2016, re-elected in 2021 and again in 2024 for a historic third term – a result that, for the first time in the history of the London mayoralty, saw an incumbent both increase their margin of victory and see a swing towards them. His landslide win was seen in large part as recognition of his world-leading climate policies. He continues to hold the single biggest mandate of any elected politician in the UK, and one of the biggest in Europe. Today, London is recognised around the world for its pioneering action to tackle the climate emergency and air pollution.

Sadiq is married with two children and still lives in Tooting, which he maintains is the best bit of the best city in the world.